Basic Science Questions for Key Stage 4

B. J. Rouan and B. C. Abrams

Book 1

Stanley Thornes (Publishers) Ltd

First published in 1991 by
Stanley Thornes (Publishers) Ltd
Old Station Drive
Leckhampton
CHELTENHAM GL53 0DN
England

The cover shows a false-colour scanning tunnelling micrograph (STM) of DNA, and is reproduced by permission of Lawrence Berkeley Laboratory/Science Photo Library.

British Library Cataloguing in Publication Data
Rouan, B. J.
  Basic science questions for key stage 4.
  1. Science
  I. Title   II. Abrams B. C.
  500

ISBN 0-7487-0556-2 Book 1
ISBN 0-7487-0592-9 Book 2

Typeset by Tech-Set, Gateshead, Tyne & Wear.
Printed and bound in Great Britain at The Bath Press, Avon.

Contents – Book 1

Preface   vi

Acknowledgements   vii

Topic 1: Investigating Science   1

1.1.1	Introduction	2
1.1.2	Safety	4
1.1.3	Making Observations	5
1.1.4	Taking Measurements	7
1.1.5	Handling Data	10

Topic 2: Life Science   15

2.1	The Variety of Life	16
2.1.1	Naming and Classifying Living Things	16
2.1.2	Many Forms of Life	17
2.1.3	Keys	27
2.1.4	A Place to Live	31
2.1.5	Feeding Relationships	37
2.1.6	Decay	43
2.1.7	Recycling in Nature	45
2.1.8	Populations	49
2.2	Processes of Life	54
2.2.1	The Characteristics of Life	54
2.2.2	Reproduction in Animals	58
2.2.3	Reproduction in Flowering Plants	70
2.2.4	The Skeleton and Movement	79
2.2.5	How Plants Feed	81
2.2.6	Diet and Good Health	88
2.2.7	Digesting Food	92
2.2.8	Energy From Food	97
2.2.9	Transporting Substances Around Organisms	101
2.2.10	Responding to Stimuli	105
2.2.11	Controlling the Internal Environment	112
2.2.12	Healthy Living	120
2.3	Genetics and Evolution	131
2.3.1	Variation	131
2.3.2	Chromosomes	133
2.3.3	Patterns of Inheritance	139
2.3.4	More about Genes	145
2.3.5	Evolution	150

(handwritten annotations: "Not seeds ½" beside 2.2.3; "Not disease ½" beside 2.2.12; various check marks beside entries; 2.3.4 and 2.3.5 crossed out)

Topic 3: Materials Science 153

3.1   Types and Uses of Materials   154
3.1.1   Solids, Liquids and Gases   154
3.1.2   Elements, Compounds and Mixtures   167
3.1.3   The Periodic Table   173
3.1.4   Acids, Alkalis and Salts   176
3.1.5   Petrochemicals   180
3.1.6   More Chemicals in our Lives   185
3.2   Making New Materials   201
3.2.1   Classifying Change   201
3.2.2   Chemicals of Life   207
3.2.3   Chemical Reactions and Energy Transfer   213
3.2.4   Rate of Reaction   216
3.2.5   Industrial Processes   221
3.3   Explaining How Materials Behave   233
3.3.1   Particles and Matter   233
3.3.2   Formulae and Equations   240
3.3.3   Chemical Calculations   242
3.3.4   Structure and Bonding   249
3.3.5   Ions and Electrolysis   253
3.3.6   Radioactivity   259

Contents – Book 2

Topic 4: Earth, Atmosphere and Space 1

4.1   Earth and Atmosphere   2
4.1.1   Rocks, Soils and Minerals   2
4.1.2   Earthquakes and Volcanoes   11
4.1.3   Weather   16
4.2   Human Influences on the Earth   24
4.2.1   The Local Environment   24
4.2.2   Global Effects   28
4.2.3   Recycling Waste   34
4.3   The Earth in Space   38
4.3.1   The Solar System   38
4.3.2   Stars and Galaxies   43

Topic 5: Forces and Energy 47

5.1   Forces   48
5.1.1   Pushes and Pulls   48
5.1.2   Turning Forces   55
5.1.3   Pressure   59
5.1.4   Moving Objects   62

5.1.5	Mass and Momentum	69
5.1.6	Structures and Materials	72
5.2	Energy	77
5.2.1	Fuels and Energy Resources	77
5.2.2	Waves	84
5.2.3	Energy Transfer	88
5.3	Sound and Music	99
5.3.1	Sound and Hearing	99
5.3.2	Audio Devices	105
5.3.3	Vibrations and Musical Instruments	108
5.3.4	Using Sound	112
5.4	Electricity and Magnetism	115
5.4.1	Static Electricity	115
5.4.2	Circuits	118
5.4.3	Electricity in Use	126
5.4.4	Magnetism	129
5.4.5	Electromagnetic Effects	130
5.4.6	Cathode Rays	138
5.5	Using Light and Electromagnetic Radiation	142
5.5.1	Shadows and Mirrors	142
5.5.2	Refraction and Lenses	144
5.5.3	The Eye	149
5.5.4	Optical Devices	153
5.5.5	Electromagnetic Radiation	158

Topic 6: Information Technology, Electronics and Microelectronics 163

6.1.1	Components and Applications	164
6.1.2	Switches and Relays	174
6.1.3	Logic Circuits	176
6.1.4	Storing, Processing and Communicating Information	181

Topic 7: The Nature of Science 187

7.1.1	The History of Science	188
7.1.2	Scientific Method	190

Preface

With the introduction of the National Curriculum, pressures on science teachers are considerable and increasing. There is more demand than ever for exercises that are instructive, easy to correct and evaluate, and which are consistent with the latest curriculum reforms.

These books have been written to reinforce the basic science required by modern syllabuses and to address National Curriculum Programmes of Study for Science. By incorporating a wide variety of question styles, we hope students can acquire the knowledge, understanding and skills required by GCSE examinations. To help students develop a clear overall view of the subject, and to understand the development of ideas and concepts, we have included questions based on Key Stage 3 material. The questions have been written for use with students of a wide range of ability.

In addition to providing a framework within which students can compile a useful set of accurate notes, alone or with the help of a teacher, this book can be used to monitor students' progress. It can also form the basis for a comprehensive revision programme – recent examination questions have been included.

Although there are questions asking students to copy diagrams, we expect that in many cases they will be traced.

Barbara Rouan
Bernard Abrams
Cheltenham 1991

Acknowledgements

The authors and publisher are grateful to BBC Enterprises Ltd for permission to make use of the extracts on pp. 44 and 152, and to the following for permission to reproduce examination questions:

The Associated Examining Board
London East Anglian Group
Midland Examining Group
Northern Examining Association
Southern Examining Group

Every attempt has been made to contact copyright holders, and we apologise to any who may have been overlooked.

Many people have helped in the production of this book, and we would like to thank colleagues for their constructive criticisms of the questions, especially to Chris Rouan for support and advice, and for allowing the use of some questions from previously published material. Finally it is our pleasure to thank our publishers Stanley Thornes, and all those involved in the design and production of this book.

TOPIC 1

Investigating Science

1.1.1 Introduction
1.1.2 Safety
1.1.3 Making Observations
1.1.4 Taking Measurements
1.1.5 Handling Data

1.1.1 Introduction

1 Name the following items used in scientific investigations and say what each is used for.

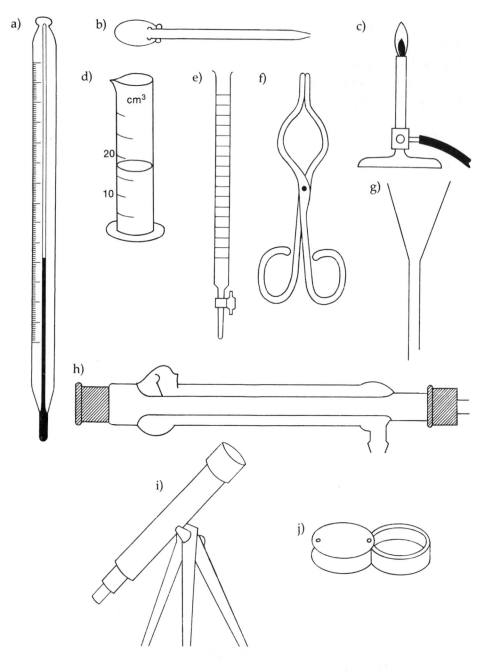

Topic 1 Investigating Science

2 Most paint brushes consist of three essential parts as shown in the diagram below.

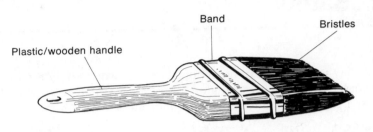

A DIY enthusiast decided to carry out tests to discover the best method for cleaning and storing brushes to leave them supple ready for re-use. She purchased four identical brushes with steel bands. The results of her experiment are shown in the table.

Brush	Paint used	Cleaning method	Storage method	Results	
				Bristles	Steel band
1	Gloss	Water	In water	Covered in paint	Rusty
2	Gloss	White spirit	Dry	Supple	Bright
3	Emulsion	Water	In water	Supple	Rusty
4	Emulsion	Water	Dry	Supple	Bright

a) Why were identical brushes used for the experiment?

b) Suggest and explain which method is **not** suitable for removing gloss paint.

c) What pattern links the **methods of storage** and the **state of the steel band**?

3 A pupil carried out an experiment to find the effect of exercise on heart rate. The heart rate was measured in beats per minute by taking the pulse. Afterwards the pupil wrote up the experiment like this:

> I stood still and took my pulse. It was 76. I then skipped for three minutes and took my pulse again. It was 120. A minute later it was 96; after another minute it was 84; a minute later is was 80. After a further minute it was 76. Exercise makes your heart rate go up.

Rewrite the account of the experiment in a more scientific way using these four headings:

Aim   **Method**   **Results**   **Conclusions**

1.1.2 Safety

1 Safety is an important aspect of laboratory work. Study the following drawing of students working in a laboratory. There are ten safety rules which have been broken. Write down as many as you can find, and say why each situation is dangerous.

2 Choose the correct hazard from the list provided for each of the hazard warning symbols:

FLAMMABLE   RADIOACTIVE   CORROSIVE
EXPLOSIVE   TOXIC   HARMFUL

a)   b)   c)   d)   e)   f)

1.1.3 **Making Observations**

1 Study the diagrams of woodlice carefully.

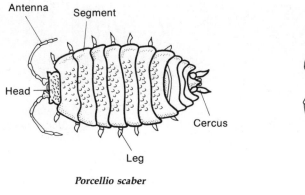

Porcellio scaber

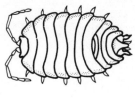

Oniscus asellus

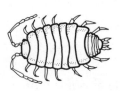

Philoscia muscorum

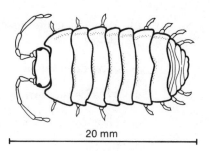

Armadillidium vulgare

a) Suggest *at least one* way in which each woodlouse differs from the other three. Ignore any differences in size.

Record your observations in a table with these headings.

Species	Observations

b) Why is size not a useful feature to choose when making such comparisons?

2 This diagram shows the main parts of a typical **light microscope**.

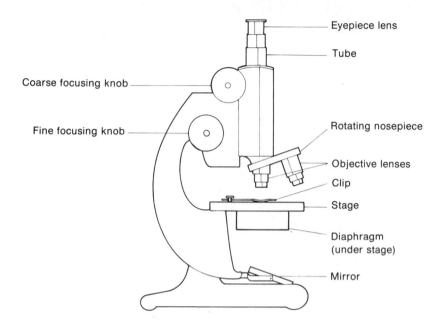

Eyepiece lens

Tube

Coarse focusing knob

Fine focusing knob

Rotating nosepiece

Objective lenses

Clip

Stage

Diaphragm
(under stage)

Mirror

Answer the following questions about how to use this type of microscope.

a) How is a glass slide held in position on the stage?

b) Why must the specimen on the slide be in the centre of the hole in the stage?

c) Why does the nosepiece rotate?

d) What is the mirror for?

e) How can you control the amount of light coming through the microscope?

f) Explain how you would use the microscope to look at a specimen under low power.

g) If you had a specimen in focus under low power, how would you go on to look at it under high power?

h) Why should you never rack downwards with the coarse focusing knob while you are looking down the microscope?

i) If the magnifying power of the eyepiece lens is ten times ($\times$ 10), and that of the low power objective lens is four times ($\times$ 4), what is the total magnification (of a specimen under low power)?

j) If the magnifying power of the eyepiece lens is $\times$ 10, and that of the high power objective lens is $\times$ 40, what is the total magnification (of a specimen under high power)?

3 The diagrams below show a specimen mounted on a slide ready for viewing under the microscope. Look at them and answer the questions below.

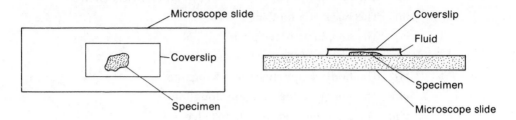

a) What is the purpose of the coverslip?

b) This diagram shows how to lower a coverslip on to a specimen.

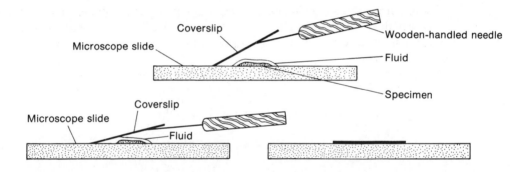

   Why is it important to lower the coverslip in this way?

c) The fluid used may be either pure water or a stain. Give one advantage and one disadvantage of using a stain.

d) Describe in *words* how to prepare a slide for the microscope. Use the diagrams to help you.

1.1.4 Taking Measurements

1 Below is a list of units used in taking scientific measurements:

        ampere   cubic centimetre   degrees Celsius   joule
           kilogram   metre   newton   second   square metre   volt

a) Write down the symbols used for each of these units.

b) Which of the units would you use to measure each of the following?

    i)   The potential difference across the terminals of a battery.

    ii)   The amount of current flowing in an electrical circuit.

    iii)   The mass of a football.

    iv)   The area of a soccer pitch.

    v)   The height of the goal posts.

    vi)   The body temperature of a kangaroo.

    vii)   The energy value of a jam doughnut.

    viii) The force needed to pull a sledge.

    ix)   The volume of coffee in a cup.

    x)   The time taken to read this question.

2   Choose from the following sets of equipment the apparatus you would use to measure the volume (in cm^3) of each of the samples listed as part of an experiment. Give a short description of how you would carry out the measurement.

Apparatus

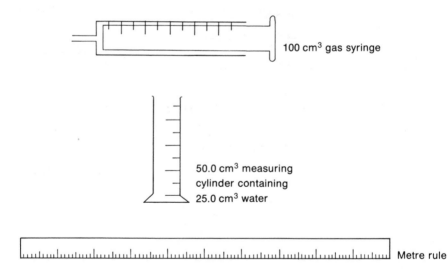

100 cm³ gas syringe

50.0 cm³ measuring cylinder containing 25.0 cm³ water

Metre rule

Samples

a) A small piece of igneous rock approximately 1 cm in diameter.

b) The gas produced when an indigestion tablet is added to water.

c) A large steel cube from a piece of machinery.

d) The air trapped in a 20 cm^3 sample of powdery soil.

e) The maximum volume of liquid which can be held by a large spoon.

3 a) Bacteria are microscopic organisms. They cannot be seen with the naked eye. Small units are needed to measure their length. The best units to use are **micrometres**. A micrometre is one thousandth of a millimetre.

$$1000 \text{ micrometres } = 1 \text{ millimetre}$$

$$1000 \, \mu m \ = \ 1 \text{ mm}$$

   i) How many micrometres are there in one metre?

   ii) The diagrams below show two types of bacteria magnified 4000 times. What is the actual length in micrometres of the two types of bacteria?

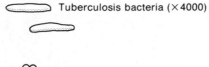

Tuberculosis bacteria (×4000)

Pneumonia bacteria (×4000)

b) Smaller things such as viruses are measured in units called nanometres. A nanometre is one millionth of a millimetre.

$$1\,000\,000 \text{ nanometres } = 1 \text{ millimetre}$$

$$1\,000\,000 \text{ nm } = \ 1 \text{ mm}$$

   i) How many nanometres are there in one micrometre?

   ii) How many nanometres are there in one metre?

   iii) By how many times has the mumps virus been enlarged in the diagram below?

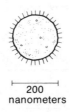

200
nanometers

c) An oxygen atom is about one tenth of a nanometre in diameter.
How many oxygen atoms arranged side by side would cover a length of one centimetre?

d) Place these units in order, starting with the smallest unit and ending with the largest:

    kilometre   **metre**   **micrometre**   **millimetre**   **nanometre**

1.1.5 Handling Data

1   The column graph below shows the variation in the number of prickles on the leaves of a sprig of holly.

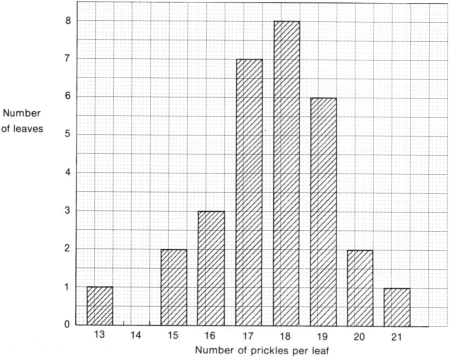

a)   How many leaves had their number of prickles counted?

b)   What is the most common number of prickles? What is this value called?

c)   What is the average (mean) number of prickles per leaf?

2   The table below provides information about the planets in the solar system. Use the information in the table to answer the questions which follow it.

Planet	Mean distance from Sun (millions of kilometres)	Orbital period	Rotation period	Diameter (kilometres)	Relative mass (Earth = 1)
Mercury	57.9	88 days	58.6 days	4 879	0.06
Venus	108.2	224.7 days	243.1 days	12 104	0.82
Earth	149.6	365.3 days	23 h 56 m	12 756	1
Mars	227.9	687.0 days	24 h 37 m	6 794	0.11
Jupiter	778.3	11.9 years	9 h 50 m	143 884	318
Saturn	1427.0	29.5 years	10 h 39 m	120 536	95
Uranus	2869.6	84.0 years	17 h 14 m	50 724	15
Neptune	4496.7	164.8 years	17 h 52 m	50 538	17
Pluto	5900	247.7 years	6.4 days	2 445	0.01

a) How far away from the Sun is Venus?

b) What is the diameter of Mars?

c) How long does it take Neptune to orbit the Sun?

d) Which is the largest planet?

e) Which is the smallest planet?

f) How much longer does it take for Saturn to make one complete rotation on its axis than for Jupiter to do the same?

g) Which of the planets are of greater mass than the Earth?

3 All humans belong to one of four blood groups – A, B, AB and O.
The ABO blood groups of a sample of 100 000 people were tested. The results are shown below.

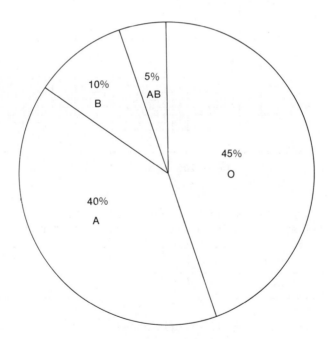

a) What is this type of diagram called?

b) Which is the most common blood group in the sample?

c) What percentage of the people tested had blood group A?

d) How many of the people tested had blood group B?

4 The heart rate of an athlete was recorded before, during and after a race for a total time of 100 minutes. The results are shown in the graph below.

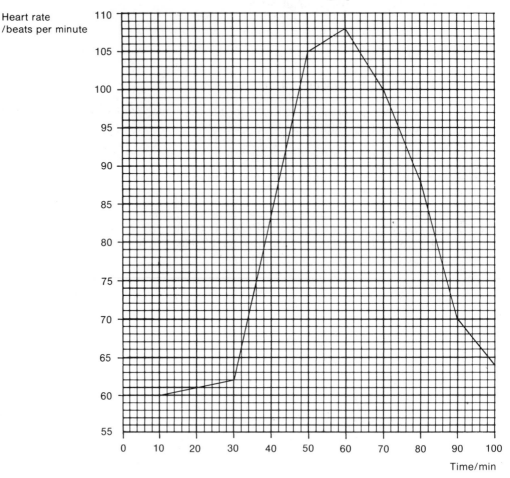

a) Using the information from the graph, copy and complete the table of data below, showing the number of heartbeats at each of the time intervals.

Time/minutes	0	10	20	30	40	50	60	70	80	90	100
Heart rate/beats per minute											64

b) Copy and complete this table about recording results.

	Advantage	Disadvantage
Graph		
Table		

5 The following table shows the weight of 32 students in a class:

Weight range /newtons	Number of students in that range
300–350	0
350–400	2
400–450	9
450–500	12
500–550	6
550–600	2
600–650	1
650–700	0

a) Draw a histogram of this information.

b) What is the modal weight range?

c) What is the advantage of displaying the information as a histogram?

6 Jane measured the time taken for the pendulum of an old clock to swing from A to B and back again using a stopclock, and obtained the following results.

Experiment	Time for 10 swings	Time for 1 swing
1	25	2.5
2	24	2.4
3	27	2.7

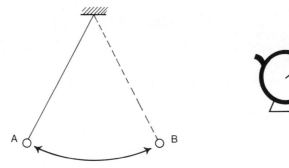

a) Why did Jane time 10 swings?

b) Why did she repeat the experiment three times?

c) Suggest one reason for the difference between the times she recorded.

d) What time should Jane use as the result of her investigation?

e) Sarah carried out a similar experiment once using a more accurate method, and obtained a time of 2.53 s. Is Sarah's result more reliable than Jane's? Explain your answer.

TOPIC 2

Life Science

2.1   **The Variety of Life**
2.1.1 Naming and Classifying Living things
2.1.2 Many Forms of Life
2.1.3 Keys
2.1.4 A Place to Live
2.1.5 Feeding Relationships
2.1.6 Decay
2.1.7 Recycling in Nature
2.1.8 Populations
2.2   **Processes of Life**
2.2.1 The Characteristics of Life
2.2.2 Reproduction in Animals
2.2.3 Reproduction in Flowering Plants
2.2.4 The Skeleton and Movement
2.2.5 How Plants Feed
2.2.6 Diet and Good Health
2.2.7 Digesting Food
2.2.8 Energy from Food
2.2.9 Transporting Substances Around Organisms
2.2.10 Responding to Stimuli
2.2.11 Controlling the Internal Environment
2.2.12 Healthy Living
2.3   **Genetics and Evolution**
2.3.1 Variation
2.3.2 Chromosomes
2.3.3 Patterns of Inheritance
2.3.4 More about Genes
2.3.5 Evolution

2.1 THE VARIETY OF LIFE

2.1.1 Naming and Classifying Living Things

1   Choose a), b), c) or d) to complete this sentence:

   To biologists, classification means . . .

   a)   giving organisms a name.

   b)   putting organisms into groups.

   c)   identifying organisms.

   d)   describing organisms.

2   Explain why biologists

   a)   i)   classify organisms

        ii) give organisms a name

   b)   Find out the scientific names of *five* organisms.

3   Here is a list of the groups which biologists use to classify organisms:

   **class   family   genus   kingdom   order   phylum
   species**

   Rewrite the list in order of size, starting with the largest group.

4   Read the passage carefully and then answer the questions which follow.

   The smallest group into which organisms are placed is a species. You would
   therefore expect members of the same species to be very similar. It is difficult to
   define how similar members of the same species must be but the best definition is
   that all members of the same species must be able to **interbreed** and produce
   offspring which can themselves reproduce.
       A horse and a donkey are quite similar organisms and they can interbreed to
   produce a **mule.** However mules are **sterile** – they cannot themselves reproduce.
   Horses and donkeys belong to different species. They do however belong to the
   same **genus** – Equus. In zoos, scientists have managed to breed lions and tigers
   together but the offspring are sterile because lions and tigers belong to different
   species. All types of domestic dogs are capable of interbreeding to produce puppies
   which will eventually be capable of interbreeding with any other dog. Wolves look
   very similar to some dogs. However wolves and dogs cannot interbreed.

a) Explain the following terms as they are used in the passage:
   i)   interbreed
   ii) sterile
   iii) mule
   iv) genus

b) What must organisms be able to do to be classified as the same species?

c) Why can lions and tigers only interbreed in zoos?

d) Explain why
   i) all types of domestic dog belong to the same species
   ii) wolves and domestic dogs belong to different species.

2.1.2 Many Forms of Life

1 All living organisms are placed into one of six **kingdoms**. These are:

Virus   Bacteria   Fungi   Protista   Plants   Animals

Into which kingdom would you place each of the following organisms?
(They are not drawn to the same scale.)

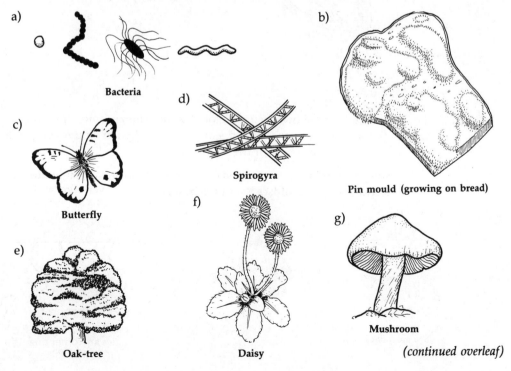

a)

Bacteria

b)

Pin mould (growing on bread)

c)

Butterfly

d)

Spirogyra

e)

Oak-tree

f)

Daisy

g)

Mushroom

(continued overleaf)

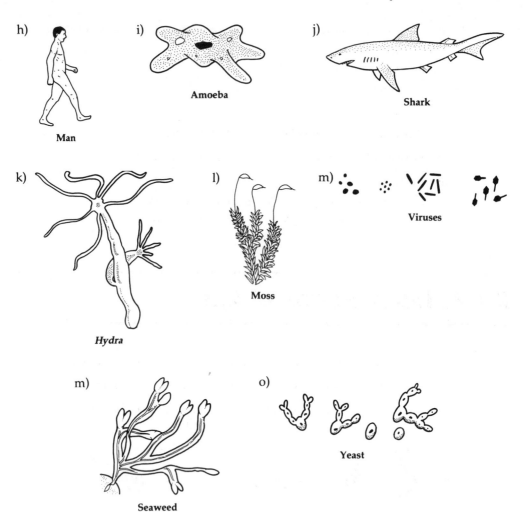

h) Man

i) Amoeba

j) Shark

k) Hydra

l) Moss

m) Viruses

m) Seaweed

o) Yeast

2 Each of the organisms shown below belong to the Animal Kingdom. They are not drawn to the same scale. Into which major group or **phylum** would you place each one? Choose your answers from the following list:

annelid worms   arthropods   coelenterates   echinoderms
flatworms   molluscs   vertebrates

a) Sea anemone

b) Acorn barnacle

c) Scorpion

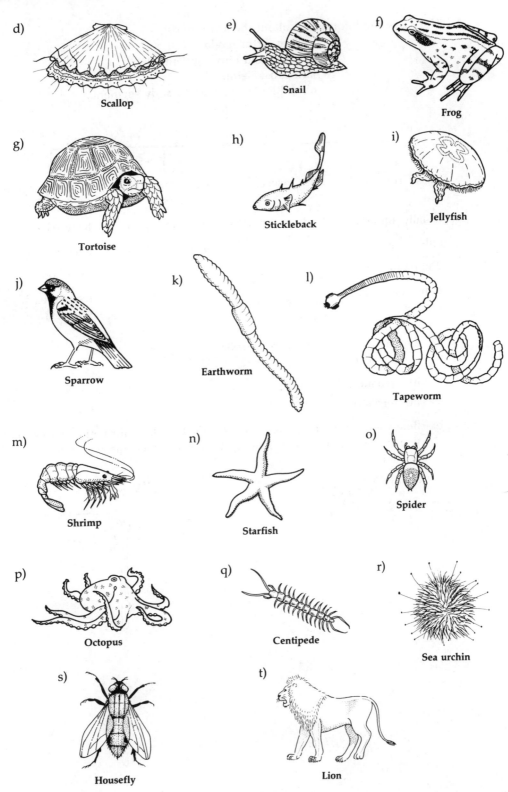

d) Scallop

e) Snail

f) Frog

g) Tortoise

h) Stickleback

i) Jellyfish

j) Sparrow

k) Earthworm

l) Tapeworm

m) Shrimp

n) Starfish

o) Spider

p) Octopus

q) Centipede

r) Sea urchin

s) Housefly

t) Lion

3 Here is some information about the arthropods:

> phylum Arthropoda
> body divided into segments
> hard **exoskeleton**
> jointed limbs attached to body segments.

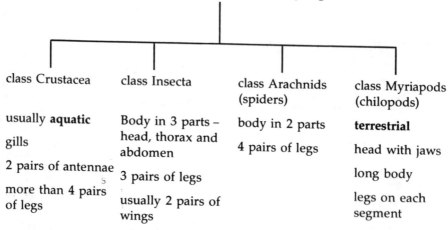

class Crustacea	class Insecta	class Arachnids (spiders)	class Myriapods (chilopods)
usually **aquatic**	Body in 3 parts – head, thorax and abdomen	body in 2 parts	**terrestrial**
gills		4 pairs of legs	head with jaws
2 pairs of antennae	3 pairs of legs		long body
more than 4 pairs of legs	usually 2 pairs of wings		legs on each segment

a) Explain the meaning of the words:

   i) exoskeleton

   ii) aquatic

   iii) terrestrial

b) Below are some drawings of arthropods. Use the information above to decide which class each of them belongs to. Record your answers in a table.

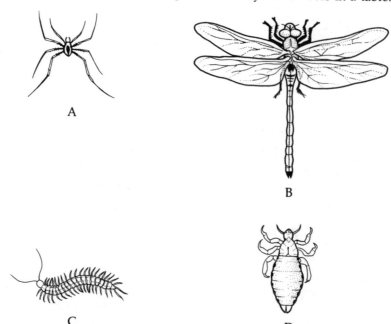

A

B

C

D

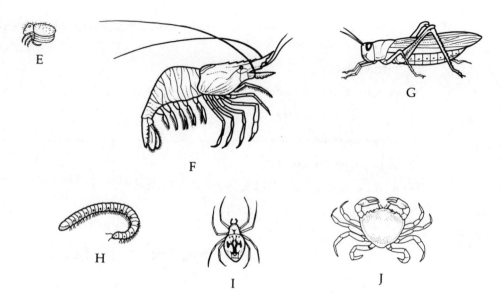

4   Explain how the following features of bony fishes make them well suited for life in water:

a) They are streamlined.

b) They possess gills.

c) They have fins.

d) They have a swim bladder.

5   Below are some observations about **birds**; suggest why each feature helps birds to survive.

a) Birds have feathered wings.

b) Their bodies are streamlined.

c) Each toe ends in a claw.

d) Their eyes have a third eyelid.

e) The gizzard of seed-eating birds contains small stones.

f) Their bodies contain air sacs leading from the lungs.

g) Their bones are hollow.

h) They often preen their feathers.

i) They build nests.

j) They look after their young.

6 Study the illustrations of birds' feet below and match each with one of the following descriptions of the bird:

a)   catches prey

b)   paddles along on water

c)   wades through water

d)   clings vertically to trees

e)   hops along the ground

Give an example of one bird for each description.

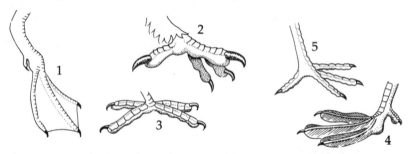

7 Match the words in the left-hand column with those in the right-hand column to produce sentences that describe some of the special features of **mammals**.

The teeth	separates the thorax and abdomen.
The pinna	are specialised for different jobs.
The diaphragm	produce milk for young.
The mammary glands	directs sound into the ear.
The middle ear	contains three small bones.

8 Answer the following questions:

a)   Where are marsupial mammals mainly found?

b)   What is the function (job) of the pouch in marsupial mammals?

c)   What is the function of the placenta?

d)   Are humans placental or marsupial mammals?

9 Give an example of each of the following:

a)   a marsupial mammal

b)   a bipedal mammal

c)   a mammal with wings

d)   a hairless mammal

e)   a mammal that lays eggs

    f)   a mammal living entirely in water

    g)   a carnivorous mammal

    h)   a herbivorous mammal

    i)   a rodent mammal

    j)   a mammal with hoofs

10   Complete the following sentences by using either **'amphibians'** or **'reptiles'**:

    a)   Frogs, toads and newts are _____.

    b)   Snakes, lizards, crocodiles and tortoises are _____.

    c)   The skin of _____ is smooth and slimy.

    d)   The skin of _____ is covered with scales.

    e)   _____ are well suited to life on dry land.

    f)   _____ must always live in damp places.

    g)   _____ use only lungs to breathe.

    h)   _____ use their skin and lungs for breathing.

    i)   The eggs of _____ are covered in jelly.

    j)   The eggs of _____ are covered in a leathery shell.

    k)   _____ mate in water.

    l)   The eggs of _____ are fertilised externally.

    m)   The eggs of _____ are fertilised internally.

    n)   _____ can regulate their body temperature to a large extent by their behaviour.

11   The drawings below (which are not to scale) illustrate a variety of plants. Study them and answer the questions which follow.

Moss

Daisy

Grass

(continued overleaf)

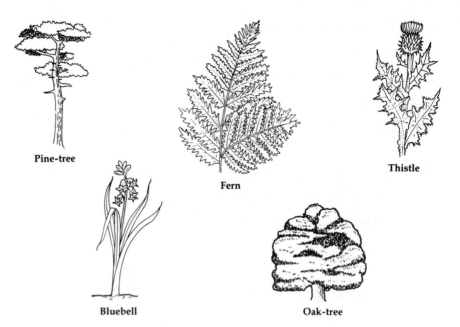

Pine-tree

Fern

Thistle

Bluebell

Oak-tree

a) Which of the plants produce spores?

b) Which one has no true roots?

c) Which ones depend on water for reproduction?

d) Which spore producing plant has leaves with a cuticle and specialised transport tissue (xylem and phloem)?

e) Which of the plants is a conifer?

f) Which ones are flowering plants?

g) Which of the plants produce seeds?

h) Which of the flowering plants are
    i)   monocotyledons
    ii) dicotyledons?

12 Complete the following sentences by using either **'monocotyledons'** or **'dicotyledons'**, or both:

a) The two main groups of flowering plants are _____ and _____ .

b) _____ have one seed leaf.

c) _____ have two seed leaves.

d) _____ have broad leaves with a network of veins.

e) _____ have narrow leaves with parallel veins.

f) _____ have a bundle of thin fibrous roots.

g) _____ have a main tap-root and short side roots.

13   The diagram below shows the structure of a bacterium. All bacteria are composed of a single cell.

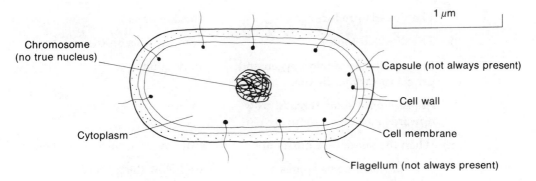

Chromosome
(no true nucleus)

1 μm

Capsule (not always present)

Cell wall

Cell membrane

Cytoplasm

Flagellum (not always present)

a)   List four ways in which this cell is different from a plant cell.

b)   What is the actual length of this bacterium? (Do not include the capsule or flagella.)

14

Pin mould (growing on bread)

A field mushroom

Pin mould and field mushrooms belongs to the kingdom **Fungi**.

Match the groups of words in the left-hand and right-hand columns to form sentences that describe **fungi**.

a)   **Some fungi are parasites but**   enzymes which digest the food.

b)   **Saprotrophs feed on**   dead material and bring about decay.

c)   **Pin mould is commonly found growing**   a spore case at the tip.

d)   **Fungi produce large numbers of**   the pin mould and field mushrooms are saprotrophs.

e)   **When a spore lands on a suitable surface**   the spores are released.

f)   **The threads, or hyphae,**   small light spores which float in the air.

g) **The mass of threads is called**   it bursts open and a thread grows out.

h) **In field mushrooms the threads**   by diffusion.

i) **The threads produce**   on stale bread.

j) **The digested food is**   from the gills on the cap.

k) **Fungal threads obtain oxygen and**   a mycelium.
    get rid of carbon dioxide

l) **In pin mould some threads grow**   absorbed by the threads.
    upwards and each produces

m) **When the spore case bursts open**   grow over the surface of their food.

n) **In field mushrooms spores are**   are below the ground.
    released

15   Copy this diagram of pin mould and add the following labels:

Horizontal hyphae   **Vertical hyphae**   **Spore case**   **Spores**

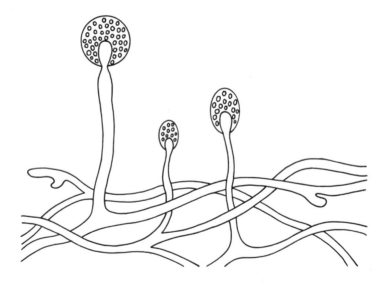

16   Explain why

a) pin mould is not green.

b) pin mould needs to produce large numbers of spores.

c) the spores are very light.

d) pin mould will not grow on dry food.

e) the threads of pin mould always stay near the surface of the food.

17 Each of the following statements describes characteristics of a particular group of
organisms. After reading the example, identify each of the groups described.

     Example: The organism has a constant body temperature, forelimbs adapted by
flying, a backbone, lays shelled eggs.

It is a **bird**.

a) Has three parts to its body, wings, three pairs of jointed legs, no backbone.

b) Has a backbone, gills, no legs, lays many eggs.

c) The simplest organisms to have a cellular structure, occur everywhere, some
cause disease.

d) Is able to photosynthesise, lives in water, has no true roots stems or leaves, no
flowers.

e) Has a body composed of fine threads, spores for reproduction, no chlorophyll.

f) Has no backbone, an unsegmented soft body, usually a shell, a large single
muscular foot.

g) Has no backbone, a long round segmented body, no legs.

h) Has hair, a backbone, a constant body temperature, suckles its young.

i) Has no backbone, two parts to its body, eight jointed legs.

j) Photosynthesises, has flowers for reproduction, broad leaves with branched
veins, one main root.

2.1.3 Keys

1 a) Look at the six illustrations of insects, labelled A–F. Use the key overleaf to
identify each of the insects.

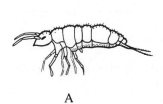

A

B

(continued overleaf)

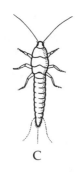

C

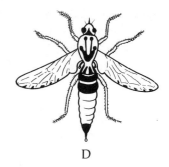

D

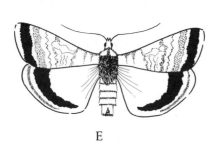

E

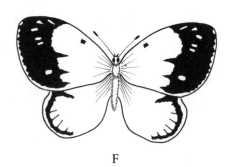

F

KEY

1. a) wings absent   – go to number 2
    b) wings present   – go to number 3

2. a) three tail filaments   – silverfish
    b) two tail filaments   – springtail

3. a) one pair of wings   – go to number 4
    b) two pairs of wings   – go to number 5

4. a) end of abdomen pointed   – robber fly
    b) end of abdomen not pointed – go to number 6

5. a) club-shaped antennae   – clouded yellow butterfly
    b) pointed antennae   – large yellow moth

6. a) wings larger than body   – green lacewing
    b) wings shorter than body   – hoverfly

b) Look again at the illustrations of the six insects.

    i) If you found one of these insects, what visible characteristics would help you to decide that it was an insect?

    ii) What visible characteristics helped you to identify insects A, B and C using the key?

2 Bacteria are identified by differences in their shape. Several shapes are shown below.

Use the branching key below the diagrams to identify each of the bacteria. Write down the letter and name of each.

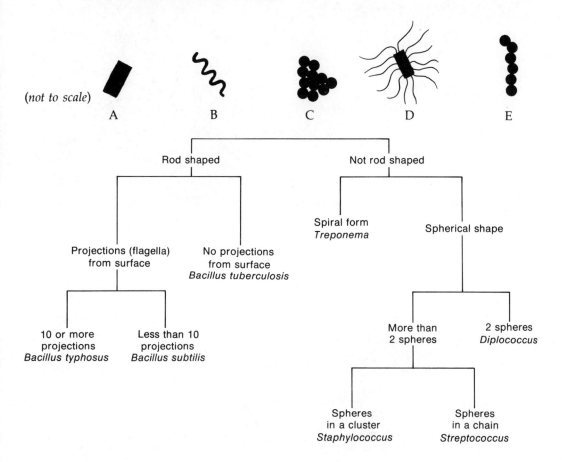

(*not to scale*)

A   B   C   D   E

Rod shaped   Not rod shaped

Projections (flagella) from surface   No projections from surface *Bacillus tuberculosis*

Spiral form *Treponema*   Spherical shape

10 or more projections *Bacillus typhosus*   Less than 10 projections *Bacillus subtilis*

More than 2 spheres   2 spheres *Diplococcus*

Spheres in a cluster *Staphylococcus*   Spheres in a chain *Streptococcus*

3 The diagrams below show leaves of six different trees which are commonly found in woodland. Construct a key to identify each one.

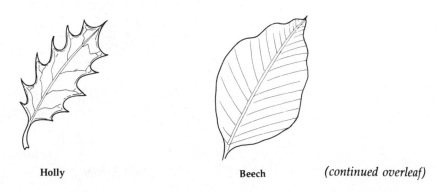

Holly   **Beech**   (*continued overleaf*)

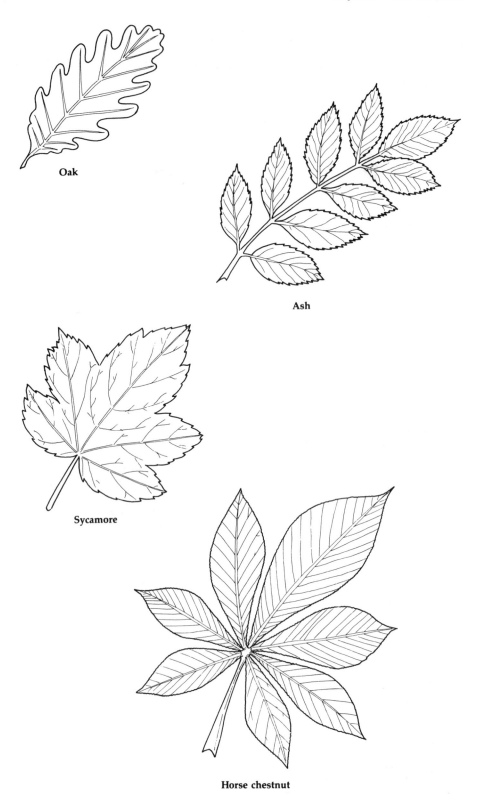

Oak

Ash

Sycamore

Horse chestnut

2.1.4 A Place to Live

1 a) A **habitat** is a particular place where organisms live. Which of the places in the list below would you call a habitat?

> aeroplane   cloud   field   hedgerow   litter-bin   pond
> pebble   stream   statue   seashore   pavement   sun
> motor car   rain   woodland   wind

b) Every habitat has certain conditions that make it suitable for some organisms to live in, but not others. Look at the following list of organisms and decide which of them would be found

   i)   in a woodland

   ii) on the seashore

   iii) in a pond

> stickleback   oak-tree   woodpecker   crab   ladybird
> oyster-catcher   heron   water-lily   leaf-hopper   winkle
> badger   seaweed   water-boatman   limpet   bluebell

c) The conditions in the habitat make up the **environment**.

   i)   Decide which of the features in the list below are part of the **physical** environment and which are part of the **biological** environment. Record your answer in a table with these headings:

Physical environment	Biological environment

> depth of water   food supply   humidity   light intensity
> parasites   oxygen concentration   predators   rainfall
> saltiness of water   temperature

   ii) Which of the above conditions are most important to a plant living in a wood?

   iii) Which of the conditions are most important to an organism living in a seashore rock pool?

   iv) Why can many species of organism only survive in one kind of habitat?

2 The environment in a particular habitat does not always stay the same. The seasons and the weather change, altering the conditions for life. These changes are often so predictable that many organisms have a pattern of behaviour which matches them. Winter always follows summer, night always follows day. Organisms may behave in different ways at different times of day or year as conditions change.

a) In what ways will the physical conditions change in a rock pool during the day?

b) In what ways will the physical conditions change in a deciduous woodland during a year?

c) Copy and complete the table below to show how some organisms respond to regular changes in the environment.

Environmental change	Organism	Behavioural response
Decreasing temperature and/or decreasing day length	Hedgehog	
	Oak-tree	
	Swallow	
Increasing temperature and/or lengthening days	Seeds	
	Bluebell	
	Robin	
	Bat	
Incoming tide	Limpet	
Ebbing tide	Oyster-catcher	
Dawn	Blackbird	
	Dandelion	
	Badger	
Nightfall	Bat	
	Owl	
	Moth	

d) Many animals produce young only in the spring. What are the advantages of this?

3 a) **The organisms which live in a particular habitat are adapted to living there.**

i) Copy the sentence above.

ii) Explain the meaning of the word 'adapted'.

b) The illustrations below (which are not to scale) show six organisms in their natural environment. For each one suggest at least one way in which the organism is adapted to living there.

Seaweed on the lower shore

An elephant in the savanna

A cased caddis-fly larva in a stream

A cactus in a desert

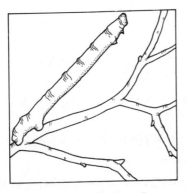

A caterpillar of the peppered moth on a twig

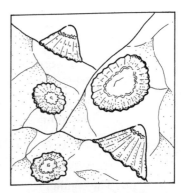

Limpets on a rocky shore

4 Read this passage which is about **moles**. Answer the questions which follow.

> Moles are small mammals which feed mostly on earthworms and often live in woods. They spend most of their lives underground and only come to the surface for a short while. A mole's eyesight is very poor, but its senses of smell, hearing and touch are very good. A mole has more nerves to detect touch than any other animal. These nerves are on the tip of its nose, on its tail and on sensitive parts of its body.
>
> A mole uses large and powerful front paws to dig tunnels. The soil which is removed is thrown out at the surface as molehills. A mole's coat can be smoothed easily in any direction, which helps it as it moves backwards and forwards through its tunnels in the soil.
>
> Male and female moles only come together to mate, usually at the end of March. The young are born in the first part of May. After five weeks they leave their mother's nest. Over the next few months they spend more time than usual at the surface. Moles usually live for three years if they are not eaten.

a) Suggest in which month a young mole is most likely to be killed and eaten.

b) Suggest *two* reasons why young moles spend more time at the surface than adults.

c) Moles are specially adapted to their underground life. Copy and complete the following table to show *three* more examples of special features and in each case suggest why this feature is an advantage.

Special feature	Advantage to moles
Very sensitive on nose, body and tail	Can sense movement of worms at a distance

5 Each of the words in the following list is defined below. Write out each of the definitions matched with the correct word from the list.

> **ecology**   **community**   **habitat**   **population**   **microhabitat**
> **environment**   **ecosystem**

a) The study of living things in relation to their environment.

b) A particular place where an organism lives.

c) The conditions, physical and biological, that are present in the place where an organism lives.

d) The living organisms of different species which live in a particular habitat.

e) A particular place within a habitat, with conditions to which certain organisms are adapted.

f) The number of individuals of a species that live in a particular habitat.

g) The habitat and the community considered together.

6 The diagram below shows a section through a pond where two samples of animals, sample A and sample B, were collected.

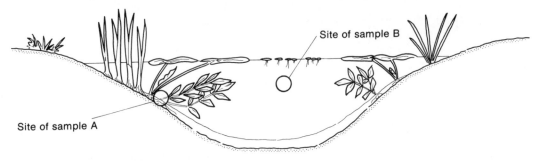

The table shows the animals collected in each sample.

Animal	Number of animals	
	Sample A	Sample B
Snails	90	2
Mites	140	80
Leeches	5	2
True worms	80	0
Flatworms	10	1
Insects – Damselfly nymphs	30	5
Water boatmen	170	45
Mayfly nymphs	50	100
Midge larvae	120	35
Beetles	30	15

a) How would you collect the animals at each site in order to make a fair comparison of population size?

b) i) Which animal was present in the largest number at site A?

ii) Which animal was present in the largest number in the combined samples, A and B?

c) Draw a pie chart to show the numbers of **insects** in sample A. (It may help to divide the circle into 20 equal sectors.)

d) Suggest *two* reasons for the difference in number of worms between sample A and sample B.

7 a) The diagram below shows a vertical section through a piece of apparatus which can be used to investigate the conditions woodlice prefer.

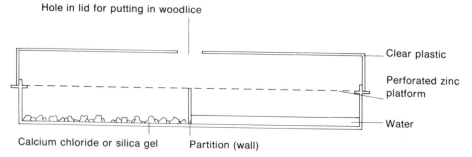

Hole in lid for putting in woodlice

Clear plastic

Perforated zinc platform

Water

Calcium chloride or silica gel   Partition (wall)

i) What is the name of this apparatus?

ii) What is the function of the calcium chloride or silica gel?

b) Ten woodlice were placed in the apparatus, and the number of woodlice in each half was counted every minute for six minutes. The results are shown in the table below.

Time/minutes	Number of woodlice in left-hand side	Number of woodlice in right-hand side
1	4	6
2	2	8
3	1	9
4	2	8
5	1	9
6	1	9

i) Plot both sets of results on one graph, clearly labelling which curve is which. Label the axes as shown.

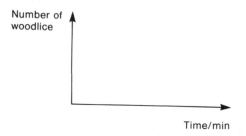

Number of woodlice

Time/min

ii) Which conditions do the woodlice prefer?

iii) When the passage between the two sides of the apparatus was blocked, the woodlice in the dry side were bunched up together against the sides. How does this behaviour help the woodlice to survive?

    c)   i)   Describe how you could use the same apparatus to see if woodlice prefer dark or light conditions.

        ii)   When such an experiment was carried out, it was found that woodlice preferred the dark conditions. How does this help them to survive?

8   a)   Why might a farm be described as an 'artificial ecosystem'?

    b)   The following table compares the total hedge length dug up by farmers during the period 1945–72, in five English counties. Study the table and then answer the questions.

County	Percentage of hedge removed	Main agricultural activity
Huntingdonshire	38	Crops
Dorset	10	Dairy
Herefordshire	10	Mixed
Yorkshire	15	Crops
Warwickshire	7	Dairy, mixed

      i)   Suggest reasons why more hedges have been removed in Huntingdonshire and Yorkshire.

      ii)   Suggest *two* reasons why hedges might be useful to farmers.

      iii)   Why are hedges useful to wild animals?

      iv)   Why does growing crops in small fields reduce the effect of pests?

      v)   Why is it better to space out the plants in a field?

      vi)   Many farmers now leave a corner of a field uncultivated. What do they hope to gain by doing this?

    c)   Suggest *three* ways in which modern farming has harmed wildlife.

    d)   Explain how the removal of one animal from a food chain or web can upset the balance of nature in a community.

2.1.5 Feeding Relationships

1   Copy and complete these sentences by choosing the correct words from inside the brackets:

    a)   A producer organism (makes food/eats other organisms/produces energy).

    b)   A consumer organism (makes food/eats other organisms/consumes light energy).

    c)   Producers are usually (animals/parasites/green plants).

d) A herbivore (eats plants/photosynthesises/eats other animals).

e) A carnivore (eats plants/photosynthesises/eats other animals).

f) The process by which the energy of sunlight is transferred to food is called (photosynthesis/respiration/symbiosis).

g) The process by which the energy is released from food is called (photosynthesis/respiration/symbiosis).

h) Microbes which feed on the dead bodies of animals and plants are called (parasites/decomposers/predators).

2   These organisms form a **food chain**. (They are not drawn to scale.)

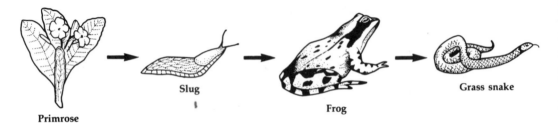

a) Which organism is the producer?

b) Which organisms are the primary, secondary and tertiary consumers?

c) Which organism is a herbivore?

d) Which organisms are carnivores?

e) Which organism is the top carnivore?

f) The organisms shown below (which are not to scale) are members of other food chains. Construct *three* food chains using them. (You may use each organism more than once if you wish.)

3   After frequent visits to a pond near their school, and a long practical study, a class of pupils identified and observed many organisms. They gathered together the following information:

> **Pond-snails feed on algae and pond-weed.**
> **Pond-skaters feed on water-fleas.**
> **Water-beetles feed on water-fleas and mayfly larvae.**
> **Roach feed on pond-snails, water-beetles and pond-skaters.**
> **Hydras feed on water-fleas.**
> **Mayfly larvae feed on algae.**
> **Water-fleas feed on algae.**

a)   Construct a food web from this information.

b)   Name the producers in the food web.

c)   What happens to the animals and plants that die before being eaten by other animals?

4   This diagram represents the numbers of different organisms in a certain food chain:

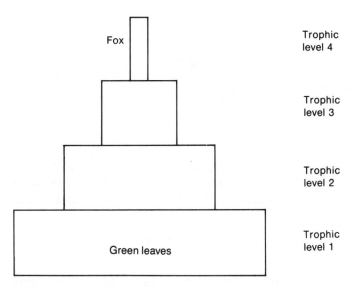

a)   What is this type of diagram called?

b)   What does the width of each bar represent?

c)   Copy the diagram and suggest organisms which could be at levels 2 and 3.

d)   The following information on numbers of organisms was obtained from an area of grassland in Michigan, USA:

producers	1 500 000
primary consumers	200 000
secondary consumers	90 000
tertiary consumers	1

Use graph paper to construct a pyramid of these numbers. Draw each trophic level to scale. (Use a single vertical line for the tertiary consumer.)

5 a) Copy the following pyramids of numbers and in each case choose the correct
food chain which it represents. Write out the food chain below its pyramid.

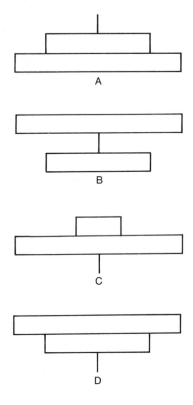

A

B

C

D

Food chains:

wheat → rat → flea   oak tree → aphid → bird
grass → rabbit → fox   cabbage → caterpillar → wasp parasite

b) i)   If the *mass* of organisms at each trophic level was measured instead of
numbers, what would the pyramid look like in each case? Draw the shape.

ii)   This is called a **pyramid of biomass**. What is biomass?

iii) Why is it important to use the dry mass in such measurements?

c) Copy and complete this table.

Pyramid	Advantage	Disadvantage
Numbers		
Biomass		

6 a) Copy and complete this paragraph (which is about energy flow).

Food chains, webs and pyramids are ways of representing the flow of _____ through an ecosystem. The original source of energy is the _____. Green plants use this energy to manufacture _____ in the process of _____. This energy is incorporated into the body of the plant as it _____. The energy is transferred along a food chain to the _____. At each step in the chain energy is lost because each consumer _____ some of it for its own life processes. During the process of decay, the energy in dead bodies and excretory material is passed on to _____.

b) State *two* ways in which energy is lost along a food chain.

c) Explain why

  i)   the number of organisms decreases at each trophic level in an ecosystem.

  ii) the territories of top predators are usually very large.

  iii) there are rarely more than five links in a food chain.

7 A knowledge of ecological pyramids is important in the production of food for humans.

a) Use the information given on the diagram below to calculate the percentage of food energy eaten by the bullock which is converted into beef.

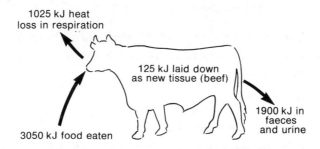

1025 kJ heat loss in respiration

125 kJ laid down as new tissue (beef)

1900 kJ in faeces and urine

3050 kJ food eaten

b) Why is the animal so inefficient at converting grass into beef?

c) Respiratory energy is lost maintaining the body temperature of the animal. Suggest ways to improve the efficiency of converting grass to beef.

d) Which of the following food chains is more efficient in providing food for Man? Explain your choice.

  i)   grass → sheep → Man

  ii) soya bean → Man.

8 The diagram below shows some of the components of a food web of Antarctica.

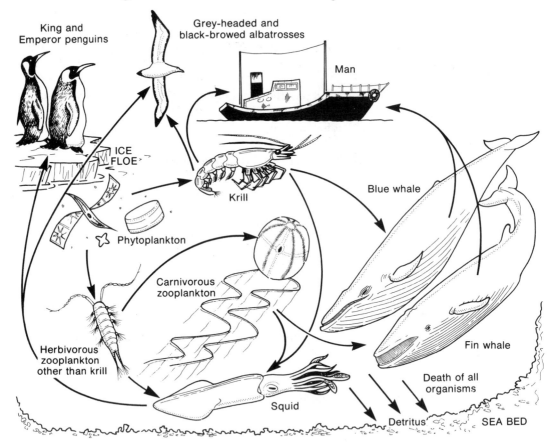

a) i) What is the ultimate source of energy for all the organisms in this food web?

   ii) Write out from this food web a food chain which involves *five* organisms.

   iii) From this food chain, name

        the producer
        one primary consumer
        one vertebrate carnivore.

   iv) From the diagram explain *two* ways in which human activities could reduce
        the blue whale population in Antarctica.

b) i) It has been estimated that 4 million (4×10^6) square kilometres of Antarctic
        ocean contain up to 70 million (7×10^7) tonnes of krill. If the krill
        population covers 36 million (3.6×10^7) square kilometres of ocean in
        summer, what is its total biomass at this time? Show your working.

   ii) Will the biomass of the phytoplankton be greater or smaller than the
        biomass of krill? Explain your answer.

   iii) In winter much of the ocean where the krill live becomes covered with ice
         and very little light penetrates. Explain how this could cause a reduction in
         the krill population.

c) Explain, as fully as possible, what will happen to the bodies of the dead organisms which fall to the sea bed.

d) Both grey-headed and black-browed albatrosses feed on krill and squid. The black-browed albatross feeds almost entirely on krill whereas half of the food of the grey-headed albatross is squid. The squid population is the more stable from year to year.

Which of the two species of albatross is likely to produce more chicks over a period of several years? Explain your answer.

2.1.6 Decay

1 a) What types of microbe are known as decomposers? What do they do?

b) What would happen to the bodies of dead animals and plants if there were no decomposers?

2 An experiment was set up as shown below.

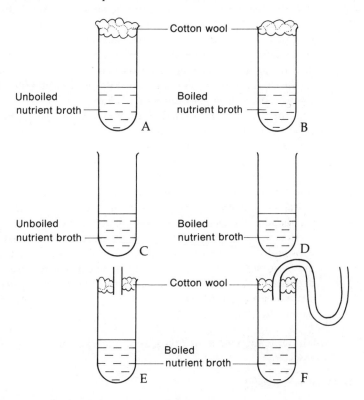

a) In which of the tubes would the broth go cloudy? Give reasons for your choices.

b) What difference would you expect in the results of tubes D and E?

c) Explain the different results in tubes E and F.

3 a) Construct a table to show the conditions required for decay to occur. Your table should look like this:

Conditions required	Reason
1.	
2.	
3.	
4.	

b) Explain why

i)   extinct mammoths have been found undecayed in Siberia.

ii) the bodies of Egyptian kings have been found undecayed in the pyramids.

iii) biologists keep specimens of animals and plants in alcohol.

4 Read this passage about fossils from *Life on Earth* by David Attenborough. Answer the questions which follow it.

> The vast majority of animals leave no trace of their existence after their passing. Their flesh decays, their shells and their bones become scattered and turn to powder. But very occasionally, one or two individuals out of a population of many thousands have a different fate. A reptile becomes stuck in a swamp and dies. Its body rots but its bones settle into the mud. Dead vegetation drifts to the bottom and covers them. As the centuries pass and more vegetation accumulates, the deposit turns to peat. Changes in sea level may cause the swamp to be flooded and layers of sand to be deposited on top of the peat. Over great periods of time, the peat is compressed and turned to coal. The reptile's bones still remain within it. The great pressure of the overlying sediments and the mineral-rich solutions that circulate through them cause chemical changes in the calcium phosphate of the bones. Eventually they are turned to stone, but they retain not only the outward shape that they had in life, albeit sometimes distorted, but on occasion even their detailed cellular structure is preserved so that you can look at sections of them through the microscope and plot the shape of the blood vessels and the nerves that once surrounded them.
>
> The most suitable places for fossilisation are in seas and lakes where sedimentary deposits like sandstones and limestones are slowly accumulating. On land, where for the most part rocks are not built up by deposition but broken down by erosion, deposits, such as sand dunes, are only very rarely created and preserved. In consequence, the only land-living creatures likely to be fossilised are those that happen to fall into water.

a) Explain why 'the vast majority of animals leave no trace of their existence after their passing'.

b) What is a fossil?

c) In what type of rocks can fossils be found?

d) Why are the hard parts of animals such as shells and bones more likely to be preserved?

e) Why are water living organisms more often fossilised than land living organisms?

f) Briefly describe two other ways in which organisms may be naturally preserved.

5 a) Choose words from the list below to complete the following sentences about decay.

> **atmosphere   carbon dioxide   microbes   nitrogen   plants**
> **simpler   soil   water**

i) Dead bodies are decayed by _____.

ii) During decay complex chemicals are broken down into _____ ones.

iii) Carbohydrates are broken down into _____ and _____.

iv) Proteins are broken down into _____ salts.

v) The simple substances can be absorbed and used by _____.

vi) The process of decay puts back into the _____ and _____ the chemicals that plants take out.

b) What is

i) manure?

ii) compost?

Explain why both are good for plant growth.

c) Peat consists of partly decayed remains of plants. It is formed in places such as moorlands where the soil is often waterlogged and acidic.

i) Why is decay incomplete in such areas?

ii) How is peat used by man?

iii) Why is it important to reduce this use of peat?

2.1.7 Recycling in Nature

1 a) Copy these sentences about the **carbon cycle**. Choose words from the following list and fill in the gaps. (The words may be used more than once.)

> **plants   decay   respiration   animals   photosynthesis**
> **combustion   carbon dioxide**

i) _____ use carbon dioxide and water to make sugars by the process of _____.

   ii) _____ and _____ break down sugars into carbon dioxide and water by the process of _____.

  iii) When animals and plants die, their bodies _____.

  iv) During the process of decay, microbes return _____ to the atmosphere.

   v) Carbon dioxide is removed from the air by the process of _____ and put back into it by the processes of _____ and _____.

  vi) When fossil fuels are burnt, carbon dioxide is returned to the atmosphere. This process is called _____.

b) Name *two* fossil fuels. How are they formed?

c) Draw a diagram to show how the processes of **photosynthesis, respiration, combustion** and **decay** are involved in the carbon cycle.

2   The bacteria involved in the **nitrogen cycle** are:

      decay bacteria   **nitrifying bacteria**   **nitrogen-fixing bacteria**
      denitrifying bacteria

a) Copy the following diagram, which summarises the nitrogen cycle, and in the boxes write the names of the bacteria active at each stage.

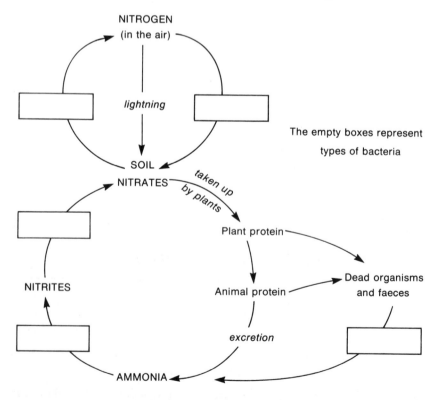

b) In the nitrogen cycle, which of the bacteria are helpful and which are unhelpful?

3 Answer these questions about the nitrogen cycle:

a) Why is nitrogen essential for life?

b) How do

    i)   plants

    ii) animals

  obtain nitrogen?

c) Why does the nitrogen cycle work better in well aerated soil?

d) Why is soil made more fertile by growing peans, beans or clover?

e) During a flood the soil will lose nitrates. Why?

4 Explain why it is important to recycle elements in nature.

5 a) Listed below are seven pairs of descriptions of respiration and photosynthesis. Draw up a table using the headings shown below and sort them into two groups:

Respiration	Photosynthesis

    i)   occurs in all cells/occurs in green plant cells

    ii)   energy is released/energy is stored

    iii) produces carbon dioxide/produces oxygen

    iv) produces food/produces water

    v)   uses oxygen/uses carbon dioxide

    vi) uses water/uses food

    vii) occurs only in the light/occurs all the time

b) The air around us contains oxygen and carbon dioxide in amounts that do not vary very much. Using the information from the correctly completed table above, explain why this is so.

6

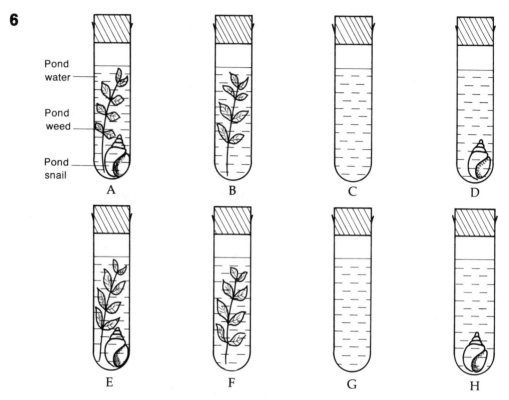

In an experiment, tubes A–H were set up as shown. Tubes A–D were kept in bright light for several hours. Tubes E–H were kept in the dark for the same length of time. Red bicarbonate indicator was then added to each test tube.

Bicarbonate indicator is used to show changes in carbon dioxide levels, which bring about a change in colour of the indicator.

$$\text{Purple} \xleftarrow{\text{CO}_2 \text{ levels decrease}} \text{Red} \xrightarrow{\text{CO}_2 \text{ levels increase}} \text{Yellow}$$
$$\text{Bicarbonate indicator}$$

a) Construct a table like the one below and complete the results for each tube.

Tube	Respiration taking place?	Photosynthesis taking place?	CO$_2$ level unchanged, increased or decreased?	Colour of indicator
C	×	×	Unchanged	Red

b) What effect does respiration have on carbon dioxide levels?

c) What effect does photosynthesis have on carbon dioxide levels?

d) Why were tubes C and G included?

e) Why were some tubes kept in the light and others in the dark?

f) In the light, photosynthesis proceeds at a faster rate than respiration. Which tubes show this? Explain your answer.

2.1.8 Populations

1 Here is a growth curve for a population of unicellular organisms. Copy it.

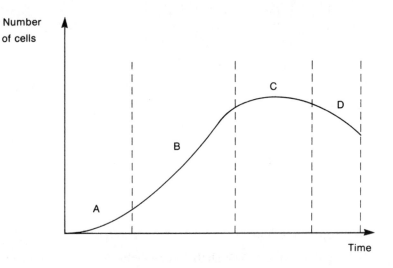

a) During which part of the curve A, B, C or D is the population growing most rapidly?

b) Complete these sentences by including the correct word or words from inside the brackets:

During stage A, growth of the population is very (slow/rapid).

During stage B, new cells are being produced far more (slowly/rapidly) than old cells are dying.

During stage C, new cells are being produced and old cells are dying (at the same time/at the same rate).

During stage D, old cells are dying more (rapidly/slowly) than new cells are being produced.

c) Suggest two changes in the environment of the cells which would cause the population growth to slow down.

d) A pair of rabbits were introduced on to an island with no natural predators.

   i) Draw the shape of the growth curve you would expect for the rabbit population on the island.

   ii) What is likely to limit the growth of the rabbit population eventually?

2 The graph below shows the population changes over one summer for a type of greenfly.

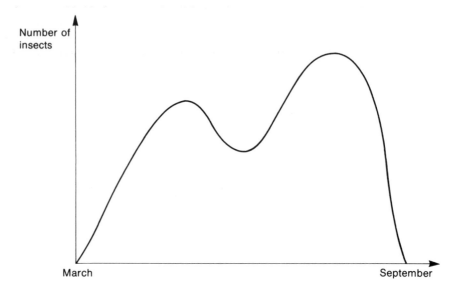

a) Copy the graph.

b) On the same axes sketch the shape of the graph you would expect if the number of ladybirds in the same area was recorded, over the same period.

c) Which insect is

   i) the predator

   ii) the prey?

3 The graph opposite shows changes in population numbers of snowshoe hares and lynxes over 80 years in northern Canada. Study the graph carefully and then answer the following questions.

a) How many hares were there in 1885?

b) How many lynxes were there in 1885?

c) i) Suggest what hares eat.

   ii) Suggest what lynxes eat.

d) What happened to the number of lynxes as the hare population increased? Explain your observation.

e) Every ten years there was a sudden sharp fall in the hare population. Suggest reasons for this.

f) What happened to the number of lynxes as the hare population fell?

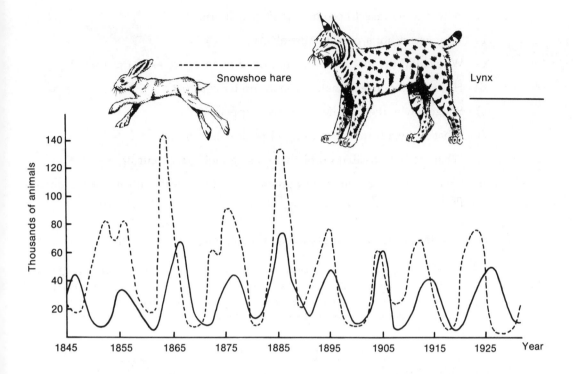

g) How might this information on the changing populations of hares and lynxes in northern Canada have been collected?

h) What does this information tell you about the relationship between a predator and its prey?

4 What is a **pest**? Make a list of *ten* organisms that people consider to be pests, and explain why each one is either harmful or a nuisance.

5 Explain the following words:

      pesticides   **insecticides**   **fungicides**   **herbicides**

6 Read this passage and then answer the questions.

In the 1860s the orange orchards of California were threatened by an insect pest which had been accidentally introduced from Australia. All the insecticides known then were useless against the insects because these had a wax-like cuticle which was resistant to sprays. It was eventually found that in Australia the number of these insects was kept down by a small species of ladybird. The Australian ladybirds were released into the American orange orchards and within two years the insects had been brought under control and the orange orchards were saved.

a) Why did the insect become a pest in California?

b) Why was it not a pest in Australia?

c) Why could the insect not be controlled by insecticides in the 1860s?

d) How was the insect finally brought under control?

e) Suggest why the pest has recently reappeared.

f) What is the advantage of using biological control?

g) What are the possible problems of using biological control?

h) Give *two* other examples of humans using biological control to keep down a pest.

7 Read the following account of an experiment and then answer the questions.

Flies were sprayed with insecticide and some died. The survivors were counted and then allowed to breed. The next generation was sprayed with an insecticide. The survivors were again counted and then allowed to breed. The experiment was repeated for eight generations and the results recorded in the bar graph below.

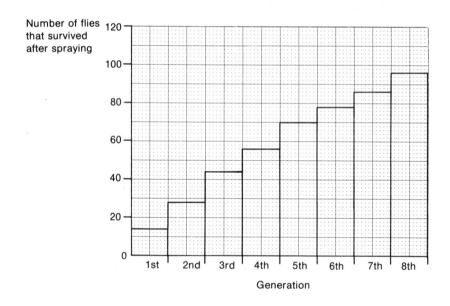

a) How many flies were alive during the third generation?

b) What do you notice about the number of flies that survive each spraying?

c) Give a reason for your answer to part b).

d) Give *two* reasons why the use of insecticides is not the best way of destroying pests.

e) What is the difference between a general and a specific insecticide?

8 Read the passage which is about herring fishing and answer the questions which follow.

> The natural life span of a herring is ten to 15 years. They are sexually mature at the age of five years. During the breeding season shoals containing 500 million fish were once common in the North Sea. Herring are fished as food for humans. The traditional way of catching herring was by using drift nets. Whilst this method was being used there was no problem with overfishing. The numbers of herring caught in the North Sea each year could be replaced by growth. In the 1950s new methods of purse-seining and mid-depth fast trawling were started. These methods can catch complete shoals, including immature fish, and this led to a very large fall in the herring population of the North sea.

a) Name *one* breeding area for shoaling herring.

b) At what age are herring capable of reproducing?

c) Why did the use of drift nets not cause drastic reductions in the herring population?

d) What is meant by 'overfishing'?

e) Why is it important not to catch immature herring?

f) Name *two* fishing methods which have led to overfishing. Try to find out more about them.

g) Why has the human demand for fish increased so much over the last 100 years?

2.2 PROCESSES OF LIFE

2.2.1 The Characteristics of Life

1 Match the words in the left-hand column with those in the right-hand column.

    respiration   producing offspring
    nutrition   movement from place to place
    excretion   releasing energy from food
    reproduction   responding to stimuli
    sensitivity   feeding
    locomotion   getting rid of poisonous waste

2 The table below lists differences between animals and plants. Copy and complete it by giving a reason for each difference.

Typical animal (e.g. a frog or a trout)	Typical plant (e.g. a buttercup or a French bean)	What is the reason for this difference?
Has feeding structures such as mouth and gut	Lacks feeding structures	
Lacks chlorophyll	Has chlorophyll	
Is not rooted in the ground	Is rooted in the ground	
Moves around	Does not move around	
Has nerves and muscles	Lacks nerves and muscles	
Has sense receptors such as eyes and ears	Lacks sense receptors	

3 Match the following cell structures with their correct description:

    Cell structure   *Description*
    cell membrane   the granular material in which the nucleus is embedded
    cell wall   a large fluid-filled cavity in the middle of a plant cell
    chloroplasts   thread-like bodies found inside the nucleus
    chromosomes   a thin structure which surrounds the cytoplasm
    cytoplasm   structures which release energy

mitochondria   the structure which controls the cytoplasm; without it, the cell almost always dies

nucleus   structures which contain the green pigment chlorophyll

vacuole   the outer boundary of plant cells; made of cellulose

4 Below are five pairs of statements about animal or plant cells. Sort them into two groups.

Animal cells	*Plant cells*

a) They are surrounded only by a thin cell membrane.
    They have a cellulose cell wall in addition to a cell membrane.

b) They have a large central vacuole.
    Vacuoles, if present, are small.

c) The cytoplasm fills the cell.
    The cytoplasm is pushed towards the edge of the cell.

d) The cytoplasm contains chloroplasts.
    The cytoplasm does not contain chloroplasts.

e) Food is stored as starch.
    Food is stored as glycogen.

5 The diagrams below show six different plant and animal cells. (They are not drawn to the same scale.)

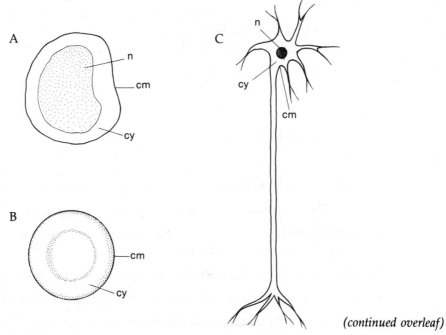

(continued overleaf)

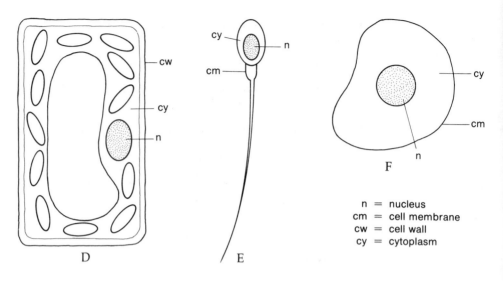

n = nucleus
cm = cell membrane
cw = cell wall
cy = cytoplasm

Use the key to identify each of the cells.

KEY

1. a)   Cell with nucleus .... go to number 2

    b)   Cell without nucleus .... **Red blood cell**

2. a)   Cell long and thin .... go to number 3

    b)   Cell not long and thin .... go to number 4

3. a)   Cell with many projections at each end .... **Nerve cell**

    b)   Cell with projection at one end .... **Sperm cell**

4. a)   Cell with nucleus more than
         half the size of the cell .... **White blood cell**

    b)   Cell with nucleus less than
         half the size of the cell .... go to number 5

5. a)   Cell with cell wall .... **Plant palisade cell**

    b)   Cell without cell wall .... **Cheek cell**

6   Use words from the following list to complete the sentences below:

         cells   tissues   organ   system   organisms

a)   Large numbers of _____ that have the same structure and function are
     grouped together to form _____ .

b)   In most _____ , tissues are grouped together to form _____ .

c)   _____ are complex structures with a particular job to do.

d)   Several different organs work together in a _____ .

7 Copy and complete the table below about the major organ systems in a mammal.

Name of system	Main organs in the system	Main functions
	Gut, liver and pancreas	
Respiratory system		To take in oxygen and get rid of carbon dioxide
Blood (circulatory) system		To carry oxygen and food round the body
	Kidneys, bladder, liver	
	Eyes, ears, nose	To detect stimuli
Nervous system	Brain and spinal cord	
Musculo-skeletal system		To support and move the body
Reproductive system	Testes and ovaries	

8

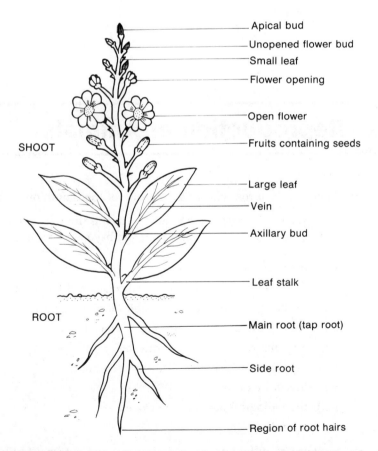

Complete these sentences, which describe the structure of a flowering plant such as the one in the diagram:

a) The plant is made up of two main parts, the _____ and the _____ .

b) The _____ is above the ground and the _____ is below the ground.

c) The main root is called the _____ .

d) Near the tip of each side root is a covering of _____ .

e) At the tip of the shoot there is an _____ bud where growth takes place.

f) _____ are flat and green.

g) Each leaf is attached to the stem by a short _____ _____ .

9 What jobs are carried out by the following plant organs?

a) the stem

b) the roots

c) the leaves

d) the flowers

e) the fruits

2.2.2 Reproduction in Animals

1 a) Match each of the following with one of the definitions below:

gamete   egg   sperm   fertilisation   viviparous
hermaphrodite   zygote   embryo   mating

i) male sex cell

ii) an organism that produces both male and female sex cells

iii) the behaviour of male and female animals that brings sex cells together

iv) the joining of male and female sex cells

v) a fertilised egg develops into this

vi) organisms which give birth to live young

vii) female sex cell

viii) the biological name for a sex cell

ix) a fertilised egg

b) Explain the difference between internal and external **fertilisation**.

c) Give the names of *three* animals that are hermaphrodite.

2 a) Complete this diagram:

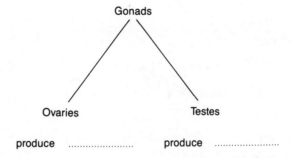

b) Use labelled diagrams to show the structure of a human egg and a human sperm.

c) Write down *four* ways in which an egg differs from a sperm. (*Clue words:* shape, size, food, movement.)

d) Use labelled diagrams to show how fertilisation takes place.

3 The following sentences are about reproduction in mammals. Copy each sentence choosing only the correct alternative to complete it.

a) The release of one or more eggs from the ovary is called

    i) copulation
    ii) conception
    iii) fertilisation
    iv) ovulation

b) The transfer of male sperms into the female's body is called

    i) copulation
    ii) conception
    iii) fertilisation
    iv) ovulation

c) Female mammals show a willingness to mate at the time when ovulation occurs. This is called

    i) breeding
    ii) conception
    iii) pregnancy
    iv) oestrus

d) Conception is the time when

    i) an egg is released
    ii) an egg is fertilised
    iii) mating occurs

e) When an egg is fertilised it divides to form a ball of cells called an

   i)   amnion

   ii) embryo

   iii) foetus

   iv) ovum

f) The young mammals develop inside the

   i)   ovaries

   ii) stomach

   iii) uterus (womb)

   iv) vagina

g) The time between conception and birth is called

   i)   the conception period

   ii) the gestation period

   iii) the menstrual period

   iv) the oestrus period

h) As the embryo develops it becomes known as

   i)   an amnion

   ii) a foetus

   iii) a placenta

   iv) the uterus

i) The foetus gets its food and oxygen from the mother's blood through the

   i)   amnion

   ii) embryo

   iii) amniotic fluid

   iv) placenta

j) The foetus' waste products pass into the mother's blood through the

   i)   amnion

   ii) kidneys

   iii) placenta

   iv) lungs

k) The foetus is attached to the placenta by the

   i)   amnion

   ii) oviduct

   iii) umbilical cord

l)   When the baby is born it passes through

    i)   the umbilical cord

    ii)   the vagina

    iii) the oviduct

    iv) the amnion

4   Explain how each of the following mammals differs in the way the young develop

        a duck-billed platypus (a monotreme)   **a kangaroo (a marsupial)**
        a horse (a placental mammal)

5   Explain why young rabbits are born bald, blind and helpless while young hares (leverets) have fur at birth and open their eyes immediately.

6   Copy this diagram of the **human female reproductive system**. Replace the letters A to F with labels chosen from this list:

        cervix   **opening of vagina**   **ovary**   **fallopian tube**   **uterus**
        vagina

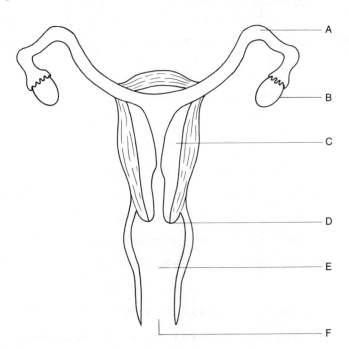

7 Write down these names of organs of the female reproductive system:

        a) **ovaries**   b) **fallopian tubes**   c) **uterus**   d) **cervix**
        e) **vagina**

Below each one, write down the correct descriptions of the organ from the following list:

    The neck of the uterus.

    It is also called the womb.

    There is one on each side of the abdomen.

    It connects the uterus to the exterior.

    They connect the ovaries to the uterus.

    The organs in which eggs are produced.

    A pear-shaped organ with a muscular wall.

    The place where fertilisation occurs.

    The place where sperms are deposited during intercourse.

    They are also called the oviducts.

    The place where the baby develops.

    An egg is released from one of them about every 28 days.

8 Write down these names of organs of the male reproductive system:

        a) **testes**   b) **scrotum**   c) **epididymis**   d) **sperm ducts**
        e) **seminal vesicles**   f) **prostate gland**   g) **penis**

Below each one, write down the correct descriptions of the organ from the following list:

    There are two of them.

    They are long coiled tubes.

    It is the loose sac of skin that contains the testes.

    They connect the testes to the urethra.

    The urethra runs through this organ.

    It produces fluid which helps the sperms to swim vigorously.

    It contains large numbers of blood vessels.

    The organ in which sperms are made.

    They are suspended in the scrotal sac.

    The place where sperms are stored.

    It becomes erect during intercourse.

    They are made up of a large number of tiny tubules.

9 Correctly match the words in the left-hand column with the definitions in the right-hand column.

Words | Definitions
| |
ovulation | the release of semen from the penis
semen | the release of an egg from an ovary
ejaculation | the sinking of a fertilised egg into the lining of the uterus
fertilisation | the fluid containing sperms
implantation | the joining of an egg with a sperm

10 Mark on your diagram of the female reproductive system

a) where fertilisation occurs.

b) where implantation occurs.

c) where sperms are deposited during intercourse.

11 About 200 million sperms are contained in the semen which is ejaculated during intercourse. Why are there so many?

12 Which of the following is the best definition of puberty? Write down your choice.

A. The time when a girl's periods start.

B. The period between the ages of 11 and 16.

C. The time when sex organs become active and secondary sexual characteristics develop.

D. The time when you become more interested in members of the opposite sex.

E. The time when a child becomes an adolescent.

13 Answer these questions about sexual development in males:

a) Write down *three* changes that occur in a boy's body at puberty.

b) Which hormones bring about these changes?

c) Where are these hormones produced?

d) At about what age do these changes usually occur?

14 Answer these questions about sexual development in females:

a) Write down *four* changes that occur in a girl's body at puberty.

b) Which hormones bring about these changes?

c) Where are these hormones produced?

d) At about what age do these changes usually occur?

e) What is the menopause and approximately when does it occur?

15 The table below shows the average heights of boys and girls up to the age of 18.

Age/years		0	1	2	3	4	5	6	7	8	9
Average height /cm	Boys	51	75	87	96	103	110	117	124	130	135
	Girls	50	74	87	96	103	109	116	122	128	133

Age/years		10	11	12	13	14	15	16	17	18
Average height /cm	Boys	140	144	150	155	163	168	172	174	174
	Girls	139	145	152	157	160	161	162	162	162

a) Draw the two growth curves (one for boys and one for girls) on the same graph.

b) In what respects are the curves

   i)   similar
   ii) different?

c) When does the most rapid growth take place?

d) When does growth slow down?

e) At what ages are girls generally taller than boys?

16 Choose words from the list to complete the sentences below about the menstrual cycle. Each word should be used only once.

   Graafian   ovulation   oestrogen   egg   immature
   corpus luteum   progesterone   womb   fertilised
   unfertilised   follicle

a) During menstruation the lining of the _____ breaks down.

b) The ovaries contain thousands of _____ eggs.

c) A single egg develops inside a _____ follicle.

d) The follicle produces a hormone called _____.

e) On about day fourteen of the cycle _____ occurs.

f) The empty _____ develops into a yellow body.

g) The yellow body is also called a _____.

h) The yellow body produces a hormone called _____.

i) If the egg is _____ the yellow body withers away.

j) If the egg is _____ the yellow body remains.

17 Match the days of the menstrual cycle in the left-hand column with the events in the right-hand column.

Approximate days of cycle	Events
1–5	ovulation
6–12	yellow body breaks down
13–15	menstruation
16–25	Graafian follicle develops
26–28	yellow body develops

18 Copy the diagrams below. Replace the letters A to H on both diagrams with labels from this list:

amnion	amniotic fluid	cervix	embryo	foetus
placenta	umbilical cord	wall of uterus		

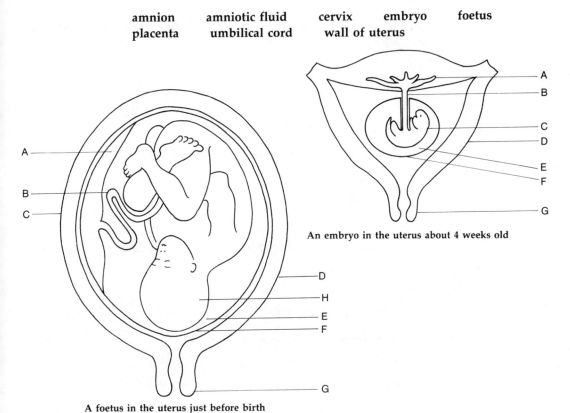

An embryo in the uterus about 4 weeks old

A foetus in the uterus just before birth

19 Copy the following sentences choosing only the correct alternatives to complete them.

a) The first sign of pregnancy is usually

i)   enlarged breasts

ii) a missed period

iii) a swollen abdomen

iv) morning sickness

b) The foetus is surrounded by a thin membrane called the

i)   amnion

ii) placenta

iii) umbilicus

iv) uterus

c) The foetus is cushioned by the

i)   placenta

ii) mother's blood

iii) amniotic fluid

iv) umbilical cord

d) Food and oxygen passes from the mother's blood into the baby's blood across the placenta by

i)   osmosis

ii) evaporation

iii) digestion

iv) diffusion

e) The waste products that pass from the foetus into the mother's blood include

i)   oxygen and urea

ii) faeces and urea

iii) carbon dioxide and urea

f) The important hormones produced by the placenta during pregnancy are

i)   oestrogens and progesterone

ii) oestrogens and insulin

iii) adrenaline and progesterone

g) In humans pregnancy lasts for approximately

i)   20 weeks

ii) 30 weeks

iii) 40 weeks

20 Look carefully at this diagram, which shows the relationship between the blood system of the foetus and that of the mother, and then answer the questions:

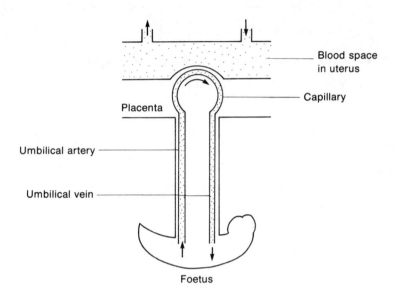

a)   Which blood vessel carries blood, rich in waste products, from the foetus to the placenta?

b)   Which blood vessel carries blood, rich in food and oxygen, from the placenta to the foetus?

21 Give reasons why a pregnant woman should

a)   attend an ante-natal clinic regularly during her pregnancy

b)   not smoke or drink alcohol

c)   not take any medicines unless told to do so by the doctor

d)   have been immunised against German measles (rubella)

e)   drink about a pint of milk a day

f)   eat a well-balanced diet

g)   wear low-heeled shoes

22 Some information on the growth of a human baby *before* birth is given in the table below.

Age/months	0	1	2	3	4	5	6	7	8	9
Length/cm	0	1	4	9	16	25	30	34	38	42

a) Draw the growth curve from this information.

b) When is the baby growing
   i) most rapidly
   ii) most slowly?

23 Babies require only milk for the first few weeks of their life.

a) What are the advantages of breast-feeding?

b) What is the name of the glands in the breasts which secrete the milk?

c) How are babies provided with food before they are born?

24 The following are the most common methods of contraception:

   **the condom   the cap or diaphragm   spermicides   the pill
   the rhythm method   IUD**

Answer these questions about the different methods:

a) What is a contraceptive?

b) Which methods prevent sperms reaching an egg?

c) What is a spermicide?

d) Which method or methods do not require a doctor's examination and supervision?

e) How can the reliability of the condom and the diaphragm be improved?

f) How does the pill prevent pregnancy?

g) What is an intra-uterine device?

h) Which method is used by the man?

i) Which method is the most reliable?

j) Which method is the most unreliable? Explain why.

k) Which method could be described as safe, reliable, easily obtained and easily used?

l) Which method also gives protection against sexually transmitted diseases?

25 The diagram shows the human female reproductive organs.

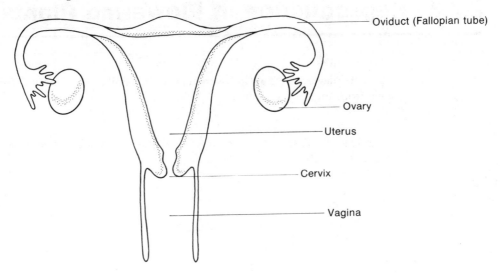

Oviduct (Fallopian tube)

Ovary

Uterus

Cervix

Vagina

a) Explain why a woman with blocked Fallopian tubes cannot get pregnant in the normal way.

b) Read the following passage and, with the help of the diagram, answer the questions below.

> A woman with blocked Fallopian tubes can now have a 'test-tube baby'. She is given hormones to increase the number of eggs maturing in each ovary. A doctor, using a fine tube through the body wall, searches for and sucks up several eggs from the surface of the ovary just before they are released naturally. The eggs are put in a culture solution in a dish. Semen containing sperm is added and fertilisation usually occurs. Three days after fertilisation, embryos of between eight and 16 cells have formed. Two or three of these embryos are gently transferred by a fine tube via the cervix into the uterus. If the process is successful, at least one of the embryos develops into a baby.

i) Suggest why the doctor wants to increase the number of eggs maturing in each ovary.

ii) Suggest why the doctor wants to collect eggs just before they are released naturally and at what stage of the menstrual/oestrous cycle the doctor would do this.

iii) Suggest features of the culture solution which are essential for a successful test-tube baby.

iv) What is 'fertilisation'?

v) Suggest why the doctor waits three days before transferring the embryos to the uterus.

vi) Suggest why, when embryos are put in the uterus, the tube is passed through the cervix and not through the body wall.

c) Do you think the term 'test-tube baby' is a good one? Give reasons for your answer.

2.2.3 **Reproduction in Flowering Plants**

1 a) Copy this diagram of a wallflower in section. Replace the letters A to H with
labels from the following list:

> **anther**   **filament**   **ovary**   **ovule**   **petal**   **receptacle**
> **sepal**   **stigma**

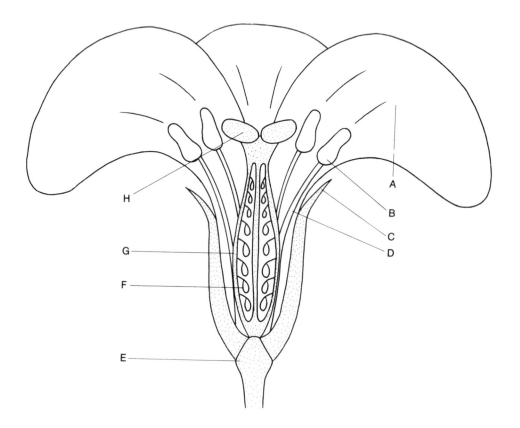

Wallflower in section

b) The wallflower is pollinated by insects. Which parts of the flower have the
function of attracting insects?

2   Match the parts of a flower in the left-hand column with their correct functions in the right-hand column.

Parts of a flower	Function
receptacle	to support the anther
style	to produce pollen
stigma	to make a sugary liquid
pollen	to receive pollen
petal	to contain the male gametes
nectary	to attract insects
sepal	to form the base of the flower
anther	to hold up the stigma
ovary	to protect the flower in bud
filament	to contain the female gametes

3   Copy and complete these two sentences:

a)   The transfer of pollen from the anther to the stigma is called _____.

b)   The joining of the male nucleus from the pollen grain with the egg cell in the ovule is called _____.

4   Explain each of the following:

a)   Wind-pollinated flowers do not have brightly coloured petals, do not have nectaries and are not scented.

b)   The stamens of wind-pollinated flowers hang outside the petals. The anthers are loosely attached to the filaments.

c)   The stigmas of wind-pollinated flowers are often feathery and hang outside the petals.

d)   The pollen grains of wind-pollinated flowers are very light and are produced in vast numbers.

e)   The pollen grains of insect-pollinated flowers have spikes.

5   Copy and complete these sentences:

a)   In self-pollination, pollen is transferred from the _____ to the _____ of the _____ flower.

b)   In cross-pollination, pollen is transferred from the _____ to the _____ of a _____ flower.

c)   Cross-pollination is much better for the plant because it creates _____.

6 Write down *three* ways in which flowering plants can ensure cross-pollination.

7 a) Copy this diagram of a carpel (the female part of a flower). Replace the letters A to F with labels chosen from this list:

egg cell   micropyle   ovary   ovule   stigma   style

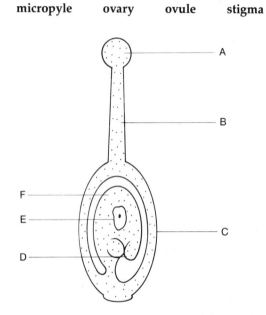

b) Complete the diagram to show how a pollen grain, once it has landed on the stigma, fertilises the ovule.

8 Copy and complete this table to show what happens to the flower parts after fertilisation:

Flower parts	What happens after fertilisation
Petals	Wither away
Sepals	
Stamens	
Egg cell	
Ovule	
Ovary	

9 Complete these sentences about **seeds** by choosing the correct word from inside the brackets.

a) Fruits and seeds are formed from the (flowers/leaves).

b) When seeds are dried out they are said to be (dormant/dead).

c) When they are (dead/dormant) seeds can survive summer drought and winter cold.

d) Broad bean seeds are found inside fruits called (shells/pods).

10 This question is about the structure of seeds.

a) Match the word or words in the left-hand column with the descriptions in the right-hand column.

seed coat (testa)	the young shoot
embryo	protects the seed
plumule	stores food
radicle	consists of plumule and radicle
seed leaf (cotyledon)	the young root

b) Copy this diagram of half a broad bean seed. Replace the letters A to E with labels from this list:

plumule   radicle   embryo plant   seed coat   seed leaf

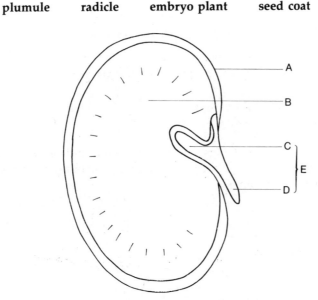

Half of a dormant broad bean seed ×2

c) If you took a dry broad bean seed and soaked it, what differences would you expect there to be between the dry and the soaked seed? How can you explain them?

d) Complete this passage by choosing the correct words from inside the brackets:

If iodine solution is placed on the seed leaves of a broad bean, they will turn (yellow/black) because they contain (sugar/starch) which will feed the (embryo/seed) when it starts to grow.

11 a) The germinating seeds shown in the apparatus below have been provided with
water, **warmth** and **oxygen**. Using similar apparatus design an experiment to test
the hypothesis that all three of these conditions are required for germination.

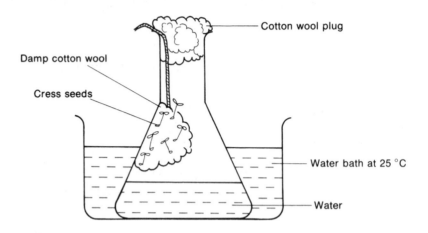

NB An alkaline solution of pyrogallol absorbs oxygen.

b) How might your experiment be modified to investigate the effect of a range of
temperatures on the germination of cress seeds?

12 The following are drawings of fruits. Copy them and next to each one write down an
explanation of how seed dispersal is brought about. The dandelion has been done
for you as an example.

The fruit has a parachute of hairs and
is blown about by the wind.

Dandelion

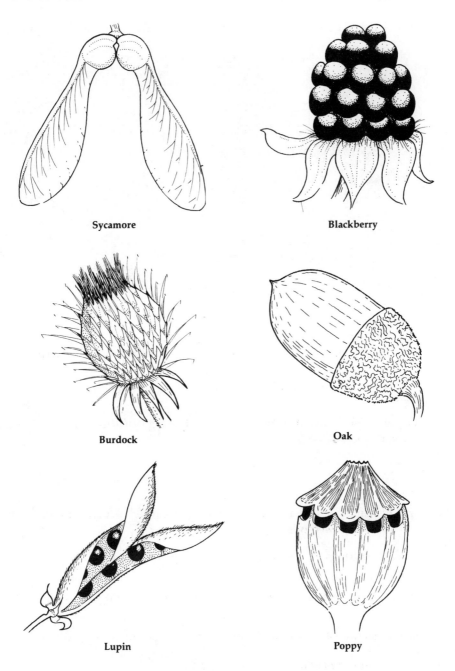

Sycamore

Blackberry

Burdock

Oak

Lupin

Poppy

13 Complete the following sentences by choosing the correct word or words from inside the brackets.

   a) Asexual reproduction (involves/does not involve) the production of male and female sex cells.

   b) Sexual reproduction (involves/does not involve) the production of male and female sex cells.

14 The diagram below shows how strawberry plants reproduce by means of runners.

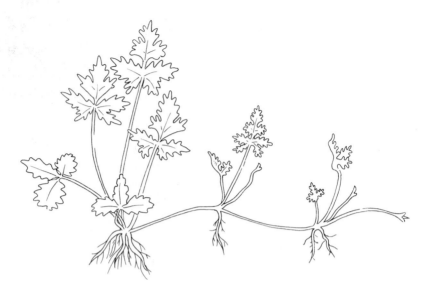

a) Describe in words how the strawberry plant reproduces by runners.

b) Is this an example of sexual or asexual reproduction?

c) State one advantage and one disadvantage of this type of reproduction in strawberry plants.

15 a) By using labelled diagrams, explain how gardeners may reproduce plants by the following methods:

  cuttings   layering   grafting and budding

b) Why do gardeners carry out the process of grafting and budding?

c) What are the advantages of vegetative reproduction

  i) to the plants

  ii) to the gardener?

d) What are the disadvantages of vegetative reproduction

  i) to the plants

  ii) to the gardener?

16

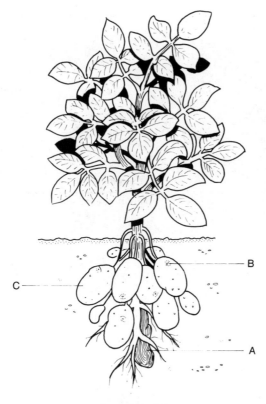

A potato in July

a) Explain why the structure A is in a shrivelled condition at this time of year.

b) Assuming that all the tubers develop, how many new plants will this plant produce in the following spring?

c) What would be likely to develop from structure B?

d) Explain why all the new plants will be identical to the original plant.

e) Food is stored in structure C.

    i)   What type of food is stored?

    ii) What chemical test would show the presence of this food?

    iii) Where and how is the stored food made?

    iv) How are the food products transported from the place where they are made to the tubers?

    v) What happens to the stored food when the tubers start to develop in the spring?

    vi) Why is the potato plant so important to humans?

17 Two chrysanthemum cuttings were treated as shown in the diagrams below:

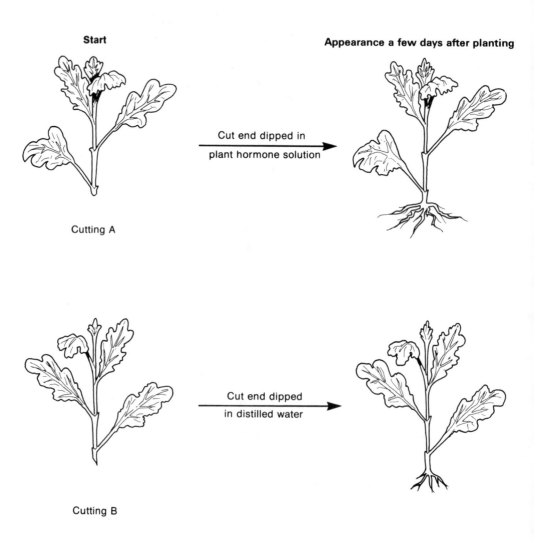

a) i)   Give *one* difference between the cuttings a few days after planting.

ii)   How would this difference help cutting A to grow better?

b) Explain why cutting B was dipped in distilled water.

c) The hormone does not keep for long in bright light or when it is dissolved in water. Suggest how a manufacturer could overcome these problems when packaging the hormone for sale to gardeners.

2.2.4 The Skeleton and Movement

1   Here are some sentences to do with the **skeleton**. The middle part of each sentence
has been missed out. Choose from the list below the best word or words to complete
each sentence. Some may be used more than once. (The first one has been done for
you as an example.)

contains	protects	are made	is made of	makes
connect	help in	works with	is protected by	

The body . . . **is protected by** . . . the skeleton.

a)   The skeleton   _____   the soft organs of the body.

b)   Blood cells   _____   inside some bones.

c)   The skeleton   _____   muscles to bring about movement.

d)   The skeleton   _____   bone.

e)   Bone   _____   calcium.

f)   Calcium   _____   bones hard.

g)   Gristle   _____   cartilage.

h)   Tendons   _____   muscles to bones.

i)   Ligaments   _____   bones to bones.

j)   The skull   _____   the brain.

k)   The ribs   _____   breathing.

l)   The rib cage   _____   the heart and lungs.

m) A moving joint _____   lubricating fluid.

2   Copy the diagram below, which represents a moving joint.

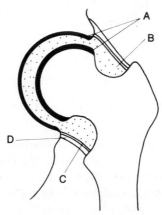

a) Replace the letters A to D with the correct labels.

b) i) What type of joint is this?

    ii) Where is it found?

c) Next to your diagram copy and complete this table, which refers to the labels on the diagram.

	Name of structure	*Function*
A		
B		
C		
D		

3 Study this diagram of the arm:

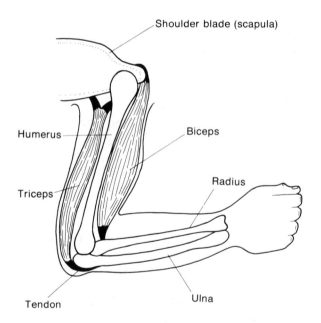

Complete the following passage by choosing the correct word or words from inside the brackets.

When you bend your arm at the elbow the following things happen:
The biceps (contracts/relaxes), becoming (shorter and fatter/longer and thinner). The triceps muscle (contracts/relaxes), becoming (shorter and fatter/longer and thinner). When you straighten your arm the (same/opposite) happens. The (triceps/ biceps) muscle will do work when a weight is lifted off the ground.

2.2.5 How Plants Feed

1 Green plants make food during the process of photosynthesis.

a) Copy and complete the following equation, which summarises photosynthesis:

_____ + _____ ⟶ _____ + _____
        (raw materials)   (products)

b) Copy and complete this diagram by filling in the empty boxes.

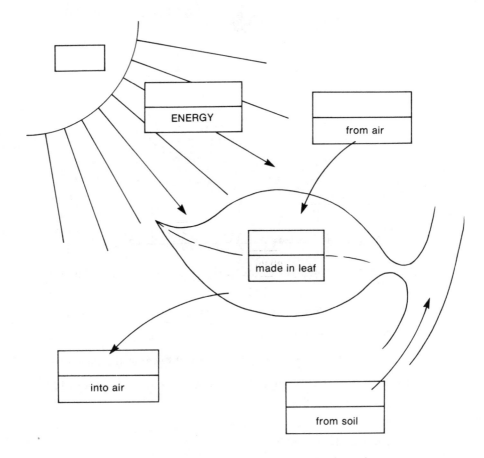

2 a) Explain why testing a leaf for starch is an indication of whether or not photosynthesis has been taking place.

b) Match the following pairs of statements and then place them in the correct order in which they occur:

Stages in the starch test	Reason
wash leaf in water	kills leaf
boil leaf in water	softens leaf
cover with iodine solution	removes chlorophyll
boil leaf in ethanol	stains starch

c) What precautions should you take when doing the starch test?

d) What colour will the leaf turn (at the end of the test) if starch is present?

3 Study the diagram below and then answer the following questions.

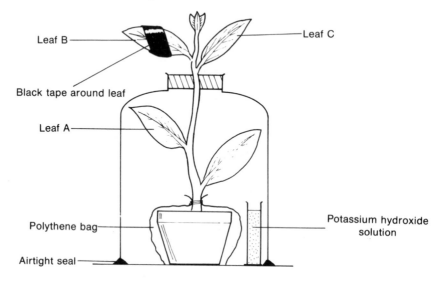

a) The plant was kept in the dark for 24 hours before being placed in sunlight. Why?

b) What is the function of the potassium hydroxide solution?

c) Why is the pot enclosed in a polythene bag?

d) Why is it important to have an airtight seal at the base of the bell jar?

The apparatus was set up as in the diagram and left for about 12 hours. Starch tests were carried out on

    i)   leaf A

    ii) leaf B

    iii) leaf C

e) What would you expect the results to be? What do the results tell you about the conditions needed for photosynthesis?

f) Which one is the control leaf and why is it necessary?

4 a) What is unusual about leaf A below?

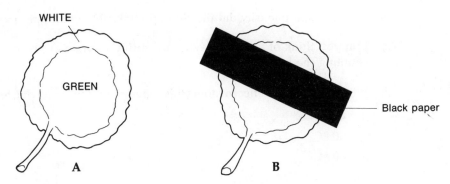

WHITE

GREEN

A

Black paper

B

b) How would you remove all the starch from a leaf?

c) Both the above leaves were destarched, then exposed to bright sunlight for six hours. If both leaves were then tested for starch in the usual way, what would they look like? Draw a diagram of each leaf to show the result.

d) What does this experiment show?

5 The diagram below shows an experiment that was carried out to measure how fast a water plant such as *Elodea* photosynthesises.

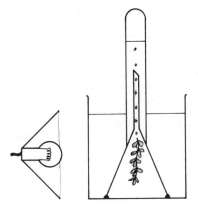

The shoot was exposed to different light intensities and the rate of photosynthesis estimated by counting the number of bubbles of gas leaving the shoot in a given time. The results are given below.

Number of bubbles per minute	7	14	20	24	26	27	27
Light intensity (arbitrary units)	1	2	3	4	5	6	7

a) Plot these data on a piece of graph paper, putting 'Light intensity' on the horizontal axis and 'Number of bubbles' on the vertical axis.

Study the diagram and the graph and then answer the following questions.

b) At what light intensity did the shoot produce 22 bubbles per minute?

c) Can you think of a better way of measuring the rate of photosynthesis than counting the bubbles?

d) What would be the effect of doing this experiment at the following temperatures?

  i)   4 °C

  ii) 30 °C

  iii) 60 °C

6 Suggest how each of the following features helps leaves to make food for the plant. Record your answer in a table as shown.

Observation	Reason
Leaves have a large surface area.	
Leaves are often arranged so that they do not shade each other.	
Leaves have stomata.	
Leaves are thin.	
The upper epidermis is covered by a waxy cuticle.	
The mesophyll cells contain chloroplasts.	
The photosynthetic cells are mainly on the upper side of the leaf.	
There are air spaces between the mesophyll cells.	
The leaf contains transport tissue.	

7 a) Make a large copy of the following diagrams about leaves and their structure.

 b) Beside the letters A to Q, write the correct labels chosen from the list below:

> air space   cell wall   chloroplast   cytoplasm   guard cell
> lower epidermis   main vein (midrib)   palisade cell
> petiole (leaf stalk)   phloem   side vein   spongy mesophyll cell
> stomatal pore   upper epidermis   vacuole   waxy cuticle
> xylem

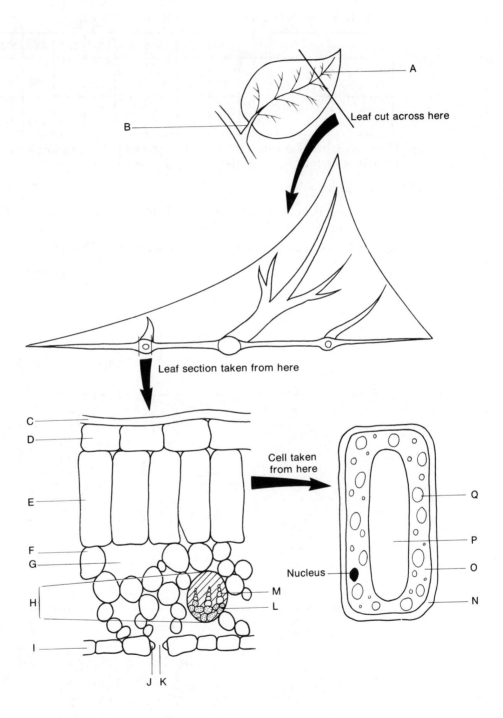

A

Leaf cut across here

B

Leaf section taken from here

C
D

Cell taken
from here

E

Q

F
G

P

Nucleus

O

H

M
L

N

I

J K

8 The information in the table below shows how the rate of photosynthesis varies with light intensity at two different carbon dioxide concentrations.

Light intensity/lux	0	250	500	750	1000	1500	2500	4000	5500
Rate of photosynthesis (0.01% CO_2)	0	1.2	2.3	3.2	3.6	4.0	4.2	4.4	4.6
Rate of photosynthesis (0.1% CO_2)	0	1.8	3.5	5.0	6.1	8.1	11.4	13.7	14.8

a) Draw a graph to show the rate of photosynthesis (*y*-axis) against light intensity (*x*-axis) at each CO_2 concentration. Clearly label each curve.

b) Use the graph to predict

   i) the rate of photosynthesis when the light intensity is 2000 lux and the CO_2 concentration is 0.1%.

   ii) the lowest light intensity to produce a rate of photosynthesis of 12.

c) How do the graphs show that the rate of photosynthesis depends on

   i) carbon dioxide concentration?
   ii) light intensity?

d) Use the graphs to explain what is meant by a limiting factor.

e) Name one other environmental factor which can limit the rate of photosynthesis.

9

The diagram shows two batches of lettuce planted at the same time in an experiment to investigate the effect of carbon dioxide on growth. Batch A had had extra carbon dioxide added to the air around it.

a) Carefully explain the observed difference between the two batches.

b) Suggest three conditions which would have been kept constant during the experiment.

c) Lettuces can be commercially grown in large polythene tunnels. Suggest two advantages and two disadvantages of this.

d) Increasing the CO_2 levels used to grow crops costs money. What must a grower consider before deciding to do this?

10 Study the diagrams and answer the questions below.

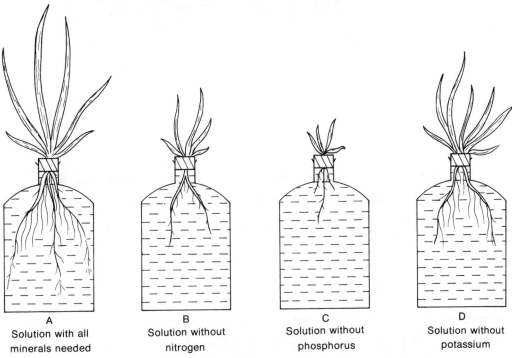

A	B	C	D
Solution with all minerals needed	Solution without nitrogen	Solution without phosphorus	Solution without potassium

A quick-growing plant grown in dark bottles containing solutions of minerals

a) Which plant shows the most growth, and why?

b) Describe one difference shown by plant A as compared with plants B, C and D.

c) During the experiment each bottle had air bubbled through it. Why was this necessary?

d) If a plant was grown in a solution without magnesium or iron, what would happen to the leaves, and why?

e) Which minerals are needed by plants to be able to convert glucose (made by photosynthesis) into proteins?

f) Why are the plants grown in dark bottles?

11 a) Copy the diagram below and add the following labels:

cell wall   cytoplasm   vacuole   root hair   soil particle
soil water   nucleus

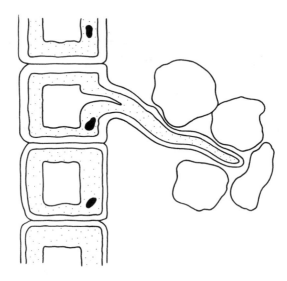

The diagram above represents part of a root in soil highly magnified.

b) How does water move from the soil into the root?

c) How do mineral salts enter the root cells?

2.2.6 Diet and Good Health

1 Using the following words, write a few sentences to explain why we and all other organisms need food:

energy   warmth   growth   repair   healthy   movement

2 a) A balanced diet consists of roughage (or dietary fibre) plus six other substances; what are they?

b) Which of the nutrients you have listed in a) are needed in bulk?

3 Copy and complete these sentences about **carbohydrates**:

a) Starch, glucose and sucrose are all _____.

b) Starch is made up of long chains of _____ molecules.

c) Carbohydrates are needed in the diet to provide _____.

d) Examples of foods rich in starch are _____, _____ and _____.

e) Sugar is found in foods such as _____ and _____.

4 Copy and complete these sentences about **proteins**:

a) Good sources of protein in the diet are _____, _____ and _____.

b) Protein in the diet is needed for _____ and _____.

c) Substances called _____ are proteins that control reactions in cells.

d) Proteins are made up of smaller units called _____.

5 Explain the difference between **high biological value** proteins and **low biological value** proteins.

6 Copy and complete these sentences about **fats**:

a) Fats are made up of smaller units called _____ and _____.

b) Different kinds of fats contain different _____.

c) One function of fat is to give us _____.

d) Many fats provide a source of fat-soluble _____.

e) Fat stored under the skin _____ the body.

f) Good sources of fat in the diet are _____ and _____.

g) It is healthier to use vegetable _____ rather than animal fat.

7 Describe how you would test an egg sandwich for the presence of

   i)   starch
   ii) glucose sugar
   iii) protein
   iv) fat.

Say clearly how you would recognise a positive result.

8 a) What is roughage (or dietary fibre)?
   b) Why is it important in the diet?
   c) List *six* foods that are high in fibre.

9 From the information below write a complete sentence about each of the following minerals we need in our diet:

Mineral	Where found (source)	Function
Sodium	Table salt	Helps to keep body fluids, e.g. blood, at the right concentration
Calcium	Milk and cheese	Hardens bones and teeth
Iron	Meat and liver	Helps to make haemoglobin
Iodine	Sea food	Helps to make thyroxine
Fluorine	Water supply	Helps to prevent tooth decay

10 Complete the following table on vitamins by filling in the spaces:

Vitamin	Source	Deficiency disease
	Carrots	Night blindness
	Oranges and lemons	
		Rickets

11 The table below shows the percentage of overweight British people in different age groups in 1981.

Age group	Percentage overweight	
	Men	Women
20–24	22	23
25–29	29	20
30–39	40	25
40–49	52	38
50–59	49	47
60–65	54	50

Source: Royal College of Physicians Report 1983.

a) i)   Which sex in which age group has the smallest percentage overweight?
   ii) Which age group has a greater percentage of women who are overweight?
   iii) Which age group has the greatest percentage difference between men and women who are overweight?

    b) i) What is the main substance stored in the body which forms the extra body mass?

      ii) Where is this substance stored in large amounts?

      iii) Give an example of a disease that overweight people are more likely to suffer from.

    c) i) Explain how your body may lose weight when it is completely at rest.

      ii) Why do you lose more weight if you take exercise?

12 What are the benefits to health of the following dietary recommendations?

    a) To consume the quantity of food and drink which will help you maintain a body weight which is ideal for your height.

    b) To reduce fat intake, especially saturated animal fat.

    c) To eat less sugar (sucrose).

    d) To increase dietary fibre to an average of between 25 and 30 g per day.

    e) To eat less salt.

    f) To reduce alcohol consumption to a moderate amount.

13 a) What is malnutrition?

    b) What are the causes and symptoms of the following nutritional disorders?

      i) obesity

      ii) kwashiorkor

      iii) marasmus

      iv) anorexia nervosa

      v) anaemia

      vi) goitre

    c) Why did Admiral Nelson insist that British ships should carry an ample supply of limes?

14 a) What is meant by a food additive?

    b) List *five* reasons why additives are used by the food industry.

    c) What is an 'E number'?

    d) How can you find out which chemicals have been added to the food you buy?

    e) In many food products, artificial colourings such as tartrazine (E102) are being replaced by natural colourings. Why is this beneficial to the health of many people?

2.2.7 Digesting Food

1

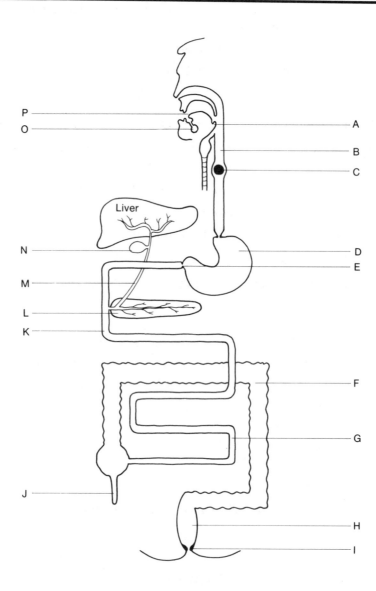

Copy the above diagram, which represents the human gut. Replace the letters A–P with the correct labels chosen from the list provided:

> anus   appendix   bile duct   bolus of food   colon
> duodenum   epiglottis   gall bladder   ileum   mouth
> oesphagus   pancreas   pyloric sphincter muscle   rectum
> salivary gland   stomach

2 From the two lists below match each structure with its correct function. (The first one has been done for you as an example.)

Salivary glands . . . produce saliva

Structure	*Function*
Salivary glands	produces enzymes which pass into the duodenum
The oesophagus	controls the passing of faeces
The stomach	produces saliva
The pyloric sphincter muscle	is where most water is absorbed
The duodenum	carries food from the mouth to the stomach
The ileum	stores bile
The bile duct	receives juices from the gall bladder and pancreas
The pancreas	controls the amount of food leaving the stomach
The gall bladder	stores waste faeces for several hours
The colon	produces hydrochloric acid
The rectum	is where most digested food is absorbed
The anus	takes bile from the gall bladder to the duodenum

3 Complete these sentences about what happens in the gut, by copying them and filling in the missing words:

An egg sandwich contains starch, fat and protein: the starch is in the _____, most of the fat is in the _____ and much of the protein is in the _____. When this sandwich enters your _____ it is chopped up into small pieces by your teeth. This increases the _____ of the food so that the digestive enzymes of the gut can act more quickly. These enzymes break the food down even more, changing _____ molecules like starch into _____ soluble molecules such as glucose. These soluble molecules can pass through the lining of the gut into the _____.

4 Copy and complete the table below.

Name of tooth	Diagram of shape of tooth	Main function	Number in a full permanent set
Incisor			
Canine			
Premolar			
Molar			

5 Answer the following questions about how we digest our food.

a) Saliva contains water together with two other important substances. What are they?

b) What are the main functions of saliva?

c) Draw a diagram to show how solid food is moved down the gullet (oesophagus).

d) What is this process called?

e) What structure prevents food from entering the windpipe?

f) Name one digestive enzyme produced by the stomach wall, and the type of food substance it helps to break up.

g) The stomach also produces acid. What is this acid for?

h) How is the stomach wall protected from the acid?

i) How does the muscle in the wall of the stomach help digestion?

j) The digestive enzymes of the small intestine work best in alkaline conditions; how is the acid from the stomach neutralised?

k) Where is bile
    i)   made
    ii) stored
    iii) mixed with food?

l) What does bile do?

m) The pancreas produces a juice which contains three important enzymes; name the enzyme which acts upon
    i)   starch
    ii) protein
    iii) fat

n) Why must food be digested before it can be absorbed?

o) Give *two* ways in which the wall of the small intestine is adapted to absorb digested food.

p) As a result of digestion what are the following foods finally broken down into?
    i)   starch
    ii) protein
    iii) fat

q) Why is roughage (or dietary fibre) important in the human diet?

6 a) Study the details of the experiment described below, and then complete the table by filling in the results that would be expected in each test-tube.

> Three mixtures contained in test-tubes were set up as follows:
> Tube A: 1% starch solution plus amylase at 37 °C
> Tube B: 1% starch solution plus boiled amylase at 37 °C
> Tube C: 1% starch solution plus acid plus amylase at 37 °C
> After twenty minutes samples from each tube were tested with iodine solution and Benedict's reagent.

	Colour of Tube A	*Colour of Tube B*	*Colour of Tube C*
Tested with iodine solution			
Tested with Benedict's or Fehling's reagent			

b) Where would you find amylase being secreted in the human digestive system?

c) Why are the tubes kept at 37 °C?

d) Where are the conditions found in Tube C likely to occur in the human digestive system?

7 A student wanted to find out if the digestion of fat by pancreatic extract is speeded up by bile. The student set up the two tubes shown in the diagram below.

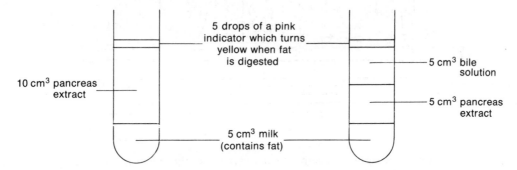

5 drops of a pink indicator which turns yellow when fat is digested

10 cm³ pancreas extract

5 cm³ bile solution

5 cm³ pancreas extract

5 cm³ milk (contains fat)

After shaking the tubes the student timed the change from pink to yellow by the indicator. The results are shown below.

Tube	Time taken for indicator to turn yellow/min
A	10
B	3

The student concluded 'bile helps an enzyme in the extract to break down the fat in the milk'.

a) Give *two* reasons why this is not a valid conclusion.

b) Give *two* ways in which the experiment could be improved so that the student's conclusion might be valid.

8 The detailed structure of the wall of the small intestine reveals many features that make it well suited to the digestion and absorption of food, as shown in the diagram below.

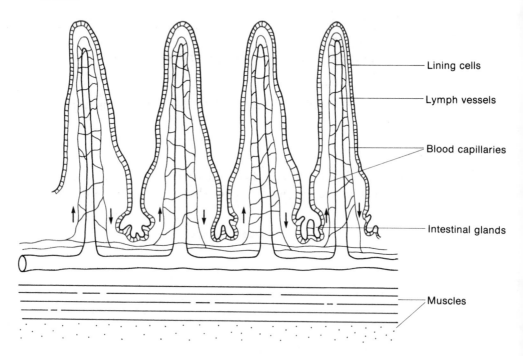

Using the diagram to help you, list as many of these features as you can, under these two headings:

Digestion	*Absorption*

2.2.8 Energy from Food

1 The energy used per hour during some activities is given below:

Activity	Energy used per hour/kJ
Sleeping	300
Office work	500
Cycling	1500
Coal mining	2000

a) List *three* activities which require energy even when you are asleep.

b) How much energy is needed to carry out the following activities?
   i) 8 hours' sleeping
   ii) 0.5 hour's cycling

2 The tables below show the recommended daily energy requirements for different people. Use the information in the tables to answer the questions which follow.

The daily energy requirements of boys and girls

Age	Daily energy requirement/kJ	
	Boys	Girls
Birth	3 250	3000
1	5 000	4500
2	5 750	5500
4	6 500	6250
6	7 250	7000
8	8 250	8000
11	9 500	8500
14	11 000	9000
17	12 000	9000

The daily energy requirements of adults

Age	Men Activity	kJ	Age	Women Activity	kJ
18–34	Sedentary	10 500	18–54	Most occupations	9 000
	Moderately active	12 000		Very active	10 500
	Very active	14 000	55–74		8 000
35–64	Sedentary	10 000	over 75		7 000
	Moderately active	11 500			
	Very active	14 000		Pregnant	10 000
65–74		10 000		Breast feeding	11 500
over 75		9 000			

a) What are the daily energy requirements of
  i)   a moderately active woman aged 25
  ii) a pregnant woman
  iii) a woman who is breast feeding?

b) i) Why does a coal miner require more energy than an office worker?
  ii) Estimate how much more energy is required in a day by a 36-year-old coal miner than an office worker of the same age.

c) i) Draw a graph to show the energy requirements of boys and girls from birth to age 17.
  ii) Explain the shape of the graphs.

3 When a peanut is burnt under a test-tube of water, as shown in the diagram, the water heats up.

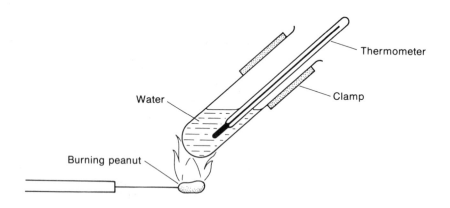

a) What property of the peanut is being measured?
b) What measurements must be taken before the peanut is set alight?
c) State *two* safety precautions which must be taken when carrying out the experiment.
d) What measurement must be taken after the peanut has finished burning?
e) State *two* ways in which the result of the experiment may be inaccurate.
f) Draw and label a piece of apparatus that could be used to produce a more accurate result.

4 a) State *three* reasons why cells need energy.
  b) What energy transformations occur
    i) when light shines on receptor cells in the retina?
    ii) when a muscle cell contracts?

5 Which of the following descriptions are true of respiration?

Respiration: Write out the correct statements.

a) occurs only in plant cells

b) occurs in all cells

c) takes place only at night

d) produces carbon dioxide

e) uses up energy

f) is affected by temperature

g) takes place all the time

h) produces food

i) produces oxygen

j) uses oxygen

k) uses carbon dioxide

l) produces water

m) releases energy from food

n) uses water

o) is controlled by enzymes

p) involves the oxidation of glucose

q) produces heat

6 a) Copy and complete this word equation for respiration.

Glucose + _____ ⟶ _____ + water + energy

b) The apparatus shown below is used to measure the rate of respiration in germinating seeds.

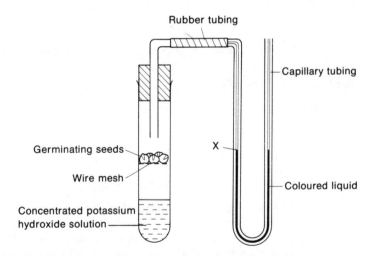

i) What is the purpose of the concentrated potassium hydroxide solution?

ii) What will happen to the coloured liquid in the capillary tubing as the seeds respire? Explain why this happens.

iii) What control should be set up for this experiment?

iv) Name two environmental factors that might affect the level of the liquid at X.

8 The formula of glucose is $C_6H_{12}O_6$. Write a balanced equation for the oxidation of glucose in respiration.

9 In what ways is respiration

a) similar to

b) different from

the *burning* of food?

10 Below are some features of aerobic and anaerobic respiration. Construct a table with these two headings:

Aerobic respiration	Anaerobic respiration

Decide which feature belongs to which column, and then complete the table.

a) does not need oxygen

b) needs oxygen

c) releases a lot of energy

d) releases a little energy

e) produces ethanol and carbon dioxide in plants

f) produces lactic acid in animals

g) produces carbon dioxide and water in animals and plants

11 Explain each of the following:

a) Panting occurs for a period of time after strenuous exercise has finished.

b) A well-trained sprinter can run 100 m without breathing.

c) An 800 m runner may not complete a race if he or she runs too fast at the beginning.

12 Read the following passage and then answer the questions.

> Carnivores adopt a variety of methods to catch their prey. Many animals ambush their prey. Others stalk their prey relying on a fast pounce or a quick chase to catch it. A cheetah, for example, can produce a quick burst of speed of up to 96 km per hour to out-run its prey. However it cannot maintain this speed for a long time and if the prey gets a good start the cheetah becomes exhausted and drops out of the chase. On sighting its prey, an African hunting dog can maintain a top speed of about 48 km per hour, in a long chase which eventually exhausts the prey. The dog then pounces.

a) What are carnivores?

b) What type of respiration does

 i) the cheetah and

 ii) the African hunting dog

 rely on in the chase to catch its prey?

c) Why can the cheetah only maintain such a high speed for a very short period of time?

d) What type of respiration is associated with

 i) speed

 ii) stamina?

2.2.9 Transporting Substances Around Organisms

1 Copy and complete the passage below which is about the structure and function of red blood cells. Choose words from the following list to fill in the blanks. (Some words are used more than once.)

antibodies	bacteria	biconcave	carbon dioxide	clotting
haemoglobin	infection	nucleus	oxygen	
oxyhaemoglobin	platelets	red	shape	tissues
variable	white			

_____ blood cells are smaller than _____ blood cells and there are more of them. Red blood cells are _____ discs in shape. They have no _____ and are packed with a substance called _____. In the lungs, _____ diffuses into red blood cells and combines with _____ to form _____. In this way oxygen is carried round the body to the _____. Here _____ is released and oxyhaemoglobin turns back into _____. Red blood cells also carry small amounts of _____. White blood cells are _____ in shape and always contain a _____. They help the body to fight _____. Some produce _____ while others can change _____ to engulf _____ which they then destroy. _____ are tiny fragments of cells which are involved in the _____ of the blood.

2 Copy and complete the following table:

Substance transported in the plasma	From	To
Carbon dioxide (as hydrogencarbonate ions)		
Digested food materials		All parts of the body
	Endocrine glands	
	Liver	Kidneys
Heat		All parts of the body

3 Listed below are some properties of types of **blood vessel**. Separate them into three groups as follows:

Arteries	Veins	Capillaries

a)   carry blood to the heart

b)   carry blood from the heart

c)   have thick elastic walls

d)   have walls one cell thick

e)   carry blood under high pressure

f)   carry blood under low pressure

g)   have thin muscular walls

h)   oxygen and food pass through the walls

i)   have valves to prevent back-flow

j)   blood flows through them in pulses

4 a)   Put the following words in the correct sequence to show the order in which the blood flows through the heart. Start with the blood arriving at the heart from the body in the vena cava.

left ventricle	vena cava	opening between left atrium and ventricle
right atrium	aorta	opening between right atrium and ventricle
left atrium	right ventricle	pulmonary vein pulmonary artery
lungs		

b) Once you have done this correctly, describe in a few sentences the route that blood takes through the heart.

c) What type of tissue is the heart made of?

d) What structures inside the heart keep the blood flowing in the right direction?

e) What is the function of the heart strings?

f) Explain why the walls of the ventricles are much thicker than those of the atria.

g) Which chamber of the heart has the thickest wall and why?

h) Why is the blood that passes through the right side of the heart deoxygenated?

i) Which chamber pumps blood to the lungs?

j) Which chamber is the first to receive oxygenated blood from the lungs?

k) Explain why the wall of the aorta is thicker than the wall of the pulmonary artery.

l) List *three* ways in which blood in the pulmonary artery differs from blood in the pulmonary vein.

m) There are many blood vessels running over the surface of the heart; what is their function?

n) Some babies are born with a 'hole in the heart', which means that there is a hole between the left and right atria. What problems does this cause?

5 Read the passages a), b) and c) below and answer the questions which follow each one.

a) The heart beats approximately 70 times per minute throughout our lifetime. Each contraction of the heart is followed by a period of relaxation. The heart is made to beat regularly by little pulses of electricity sent out from a group of cells called the pacemaker in the wall of the right atrium.

  i) Approximately how many times will the heart beat in one day?
  ii) Why is it important that heart muscle does not tire?
  iii) Where is the pacemaker? What does it do?

b) Sometimes the pacemaker does not work properly and an artificial one is fixed to the wall of the chest. This is a battery powered circuit with a wire which can be fixed to the muscle in the left ventricle. When the electrical circuit is completed a pulse of electricity makes the muscle contract. The pacemaker can be made to produce pulses at a regular rate using a transistor to switch the circuit on and off rapidly. The first pacemakers were large and wheeled about on trolleys. Later ones were smaller and powered by a nuclear source. New batteries which use lithium plates and last a long time are now used.

  i) What will happen to the heart of a patient whose natural pacemaker does not function properly?
  ii) How does an artificial pacemaker stimulate the heart to contract?

iii) What is the advantage of having small artificial pacemakers?

iv) What is the advantage of using lithium batteries instead of a nuclear power source?

c)   There are two types of pacemaker. If the patient's heart rate is too low he or she may become unconscious owing to a shortage of oxygen in the brain. A fixed-rate pacemaker is fitted which provides regular pulses at about 70 beats per minute. Some patients have problems only occasionally, when the heart changes its rhythm suddenly. A demand pacemaker can be fitted. This has a sensor which detects when the heart is not beating properly on its own. The pacemaker is switched on only when required.

i)   What would most likely happen to these patients if artificial pacemakers were not available?

ii)   Why does a low heart rate deprive the brain of oxygen?

iii)   What is the purpose of the sensor in the demand pacemaker?

6

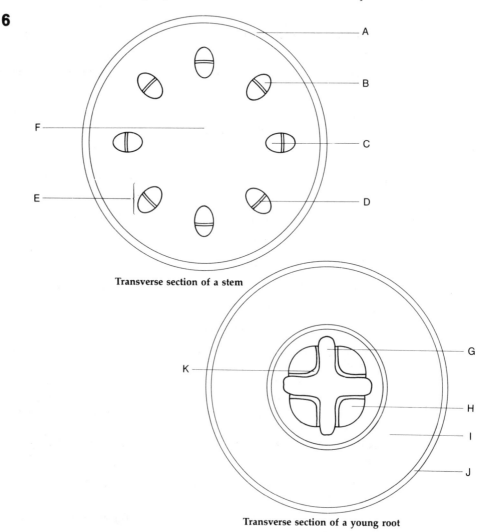

Transverse section of a stem

Transverse section of a young root

a) Copy the diagrams and write beside the letters A to K the correct tissue name from the list below. (You may use some words more than once.)

   cambium   epidermis   packing tissue (parenchyma)   phloem
   vascular bundle   xylem

b) Suppose the sections above were taken from a plant that had had its roots placed for at least 12 hours in water containing a red dye. Shade on your drawing the areas that would appear red.

c) What differences can you see between the arrangement of **xylem** and **phloem** in the root and the stem? Suggest the reasons for this. (*Clue words:* support, flexible.)

7 Match the following phrases to make sentences. Each sentence should begin with the phrase on the left and finish with one of the phrases on the right.

a) **The vascular bundles of plants are made up of**   and they contain cytoplasm and sieve plates.

b) **Xylem vessels are dead cells and**   in the sieve tubes of the phloem.

c) **Phloem sieve tubes are living cells**   xylem and phloem tissues.

d) **Water and mineral salts are transported**   their walls are supported by lignin.

e) **Sugars are transported around the plant**   in the xylem vessels.

2.2.10 Responding to Stimuli

1 a) What is a stimulus?

b) Copy and complete this table about the **senses of the body**. Some of the gaps have already been filled in for you.

Name of sense receptor/organ	Where is it found in the body?	What is it sensitive to?
Touch receptor	Skin	
Pain receptor		
		Temperature
	Tongue	
	On the front of the head	Light
Ear		
	Nose	

2 Match the following groups of words to make correct sentences about the nervous system. Each sentence should begin with the words on the left and finish with the words on the right.

a) **The job of the nervous system**   sensory and motor nerve fibres.

b) **The central nervous system (CNS)**   is to carry nerve messages around the body.

c) **Nerves connect the CNS**   little electrical pulses.

d) **Nerve messages are**   is composed of the brain and spinal cord.

e) **Nerves are made up of**   to all parts of the body.

3 a) Copy and complete the following sentences, filling in the missing words:

When our receptors are stimulated _____ nerve cells relay the message to the central nervous system. Here the _____ is sorted out. Messages are then relayed from the CNS to our muscles along _____ nerve cells. Muscles respond by _____.

b) Below is a simplified diagram of part of the nervous system.

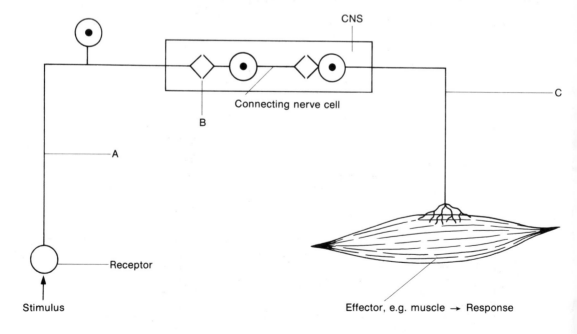

Copy the diagram. Replace the letters A to C with the correct label chosen from the list below.

   sensory nerve cell   synapse   motor nerve cell

Also on the diagram, use arrows to show the direction in which the message travels.

c) Name one other type of effector and say how it would respond to a stimulus.

4 a) Copy the following diagram of a **motor nerve cell**:

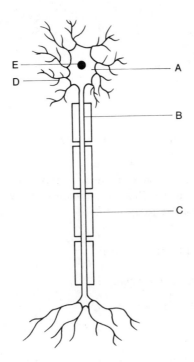

b) Replace the letters A–E with the correct label chosen from the list below.

   axon   cell body   dendrites   myelin sheath   nucleus

c) Copy the table below. For each of the features given in the table below suggest a reason.

Feature	Reason
Some nerve cells can be over 1 metre in length.	
Many branches protrude from a nerve cell.	
The axon is surrounded by a layer of fat.	

5 a) Copy the following diagram of a reflex arc:

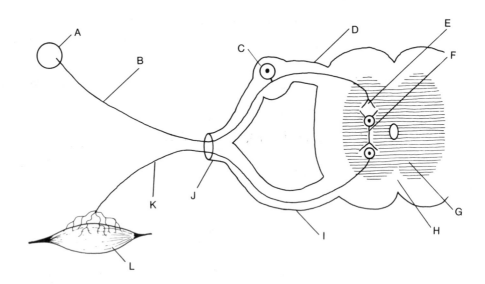

b) Replace the letters A to L with the correct label chosen from the list below.

> **dorsal root**   **ganglion**   **grey matter in spinal cord**   **spinal nerve**
> **intermediary nerve fibre**   **motor nerve fibre**   **muscle**   **receptor**
> **sensory nerve fibre**   **synapse**   **ventral root**
> **white matter in spinal cord**

c) What would be the result if

  i) the dorsal root was cut?

  ii) the ventral root was cut?

6 Copy and complete the table of reflex actions below.

Reflex	Stimulus	Response
Coughing	Irritant in the throat	
		Soft palate is raised; epiglottis closed; peristalsis
	Object coming towards the eye	
Withdrawal		
	Pressure/pain on the knee	
Pupil contraction/dilation		Contraction of muscles of iris

7 The diagrams below show a mammalian eye as seen from the front.

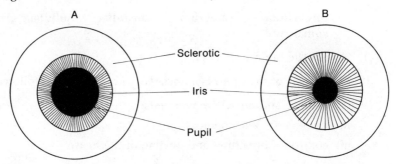

a)   What environmental change would cause the alteration from A to B?

b)   Explain fully how the nervous system and muscles bring about this alteration.

8 Distinguish between each of the following pairs:

a)   receptor/effector

b)   neurone/nerve

c)   sensory receptor/sense organ

d)   reflex action/reflex arc

e)   sensory neurone/motor neurone

f)   central nervous system/peripheral nervous system

g)   spinal nerves/cranial nerves

9 a)   Copy the following diagram of the human brain:

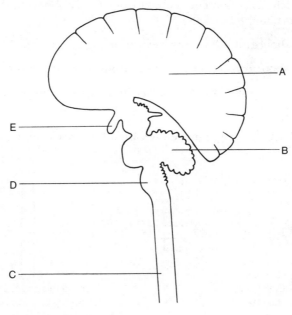

b)   Replace the letters A–E with the correct labels chosen from the list below.

    cerebellum   **cerebrum**   **medulla**   **pituitary gland**
    spinal cord

c)   How is the brain protected?

d)   Which part of the brain is associated with each of the following functions?

    i)   balance and muscle movements

    ii)   intelligence and memory

    iii) control of breathing and beating of the heart

10   Match the following groups of words to make correct sentences:

a)   **Plants and animals respond to**   quite quickly.

b)   **Animals usually respond**   changes in their environment.

c)   **Plants usually respond**   using their muscles.

d)   **Most animals move about**   more slowly.

e)   **Plants are usually fixed**   tropisms.

f)   **Plants grow either towards**   geotropism.

g)   **Plant growth responses are called**   in one place.

h)   **A plant's growth response to light is called**   or away from a stimulus.

i)   **A plant's growth response to gravity is called** phototropism.

11   Complete these sentences about tropisms by choosing the correct word or words from inside the brackets.

a)   A shoot grows (towards/away from) light and is said to be positively phototropic.

b)   A shoot grows (towards/away from) gravity and is called negatively geotropic.

c)   A root grows (towards/away from) gravity and is called positively geotropic.

12 a)   Study the diagrams below carefully. What would you expect to happen, and why?

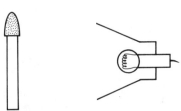

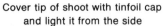
Cover tip of shoot with tinfoil cap
and light it from the side

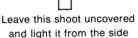
Leave this shoot uncovered
and light it from the side

b) Look at the diagrams below. What does this experiment tell you about the tip of the shoot and the part it plays in growth?

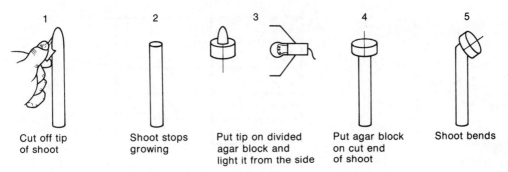

1 Cut off tip of shoot

2 Shoot stops growing

3 Put tip on divided agar block and light it from the side

4 Put agar block on cut end of shoot

5 Shoot bends

c) Look at the diagrams below. How would you explain the results of this experiment?

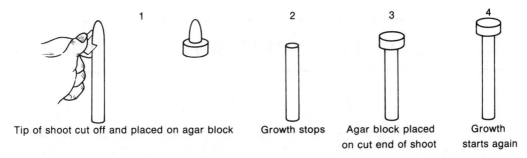

Tip of shoot cut off and placed on agar block

2 Growth stops

3 Agar block placed on cut end of shoot

4 Growth starts again

13 Complete the following passage by filling in the missing words:

The _____ of the shoot produces a hormone called _____. This hormone causes cells behind the tip to _____. When the shoot is lit from one side, more _____ gathers on the dark side. Therefore the cells there grow _____ and the shoot bends _____ the light.

14 Here is a diagram of a bean seedling whose shoot and root have been marked at regular intervals:

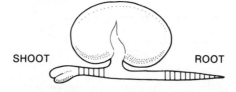

SHOOT   ROOT

a) Draw a diagram to show how this bean seedling would look after being left in this position for three days.

b) Explain the reason for its appearance after this time.

15 Copy and complete the table below which is about the growth of a plant shoot towards the light.

Stimulus	Light
Receptor	
Co-ordinator	
Effector	
Response	

2.2.11 Controlling the Internal Environment

1 The nervous system and the endocrine system are both involved in controlling the internal environment.

Copy and complete the table below which compares the two systems.

Endocrine system	Nervous system
	Messages transmitted in the form of electrical impulses
Messages transmitted through the blood system	
Messages travel relatively slowly	
	The response is very quick
	The response is short-lived

2 Copy the diagram of the human body and on it show the positions of the following endocrine glands:

   **pituitary gland   thyroid gland   adrenal glands   pancreas
   ovaries   testes**

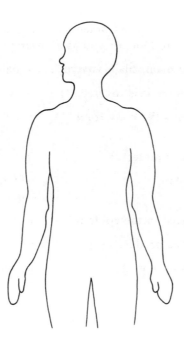

3 a) Make a large copy of the diagram below, which represents a section through the skin of a mammal.

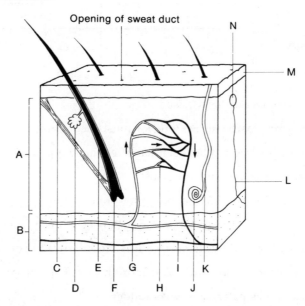

Opening of sweat duct

b) Replace the letters A–N with the correct label chosen from the following list:

artery   capillaries   dermis   epidermis   erector muscle
fat   hair   hair follicle   nerve   sebaceous (oil) gland
sense organ   sweat duct   sweat gland   vein

4 Match the following words and phrases to make correct sentences about the skin. The first one has been done for you as an example.

          The skin of mammals is covered . . . in hairs.

a) **The skin of mammals is covered**   provides insulation.

b) **The skin prevents the body from drying up**   body temperature.

c) **The skin helps to protect**   in hairs.

d) **Fat below the skin**   which keeps the hair and skin soft and supple.

e) **Melanin produced in the epidermis**   because it is waterproof.

f) **Sebaceous glands produce oil**   the body from germs.

g) **The skin helps to control**   protects the body from ultra-violet rays.

5 Below are some phrases about the skin and temperature control. Consider each pair and decide which one goes into which column of the following table.

If it is cold	*If it is hot*

a) hairs lowered/hairs raised

b) erector muscle relaxes/erector muscle contracts

c) more air trapped between hairs/less air trapped between hairs

d) much heat lost/little heat lost

e) goose-pimples formed/no goose-pimples formed

f) surface blood vessels become narrower/surface blood vessels become wider

g) more blood flows to surface/less blood flows to surface

h) less heat radiates from skin/more heat radiates from skin

i) skin looks paler/skin looks redder

j) sweat glands active/sweat glands inactive

k) heat lost by evaporation/no heat lost by evaporation

l) metabolic rate increases/metabolic rate does not increase

m) shivering occurs/shivering does not occur

6

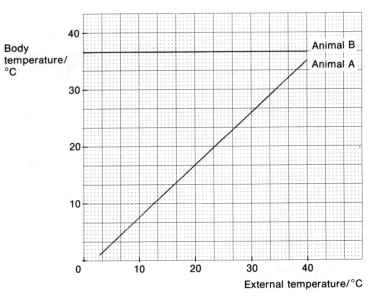

The graph shows how the body temperature of two different animals varies with the external temperature.

a)   Which animal A or B is homoiothermic? Explain your answer.

b)   Which of the animals could be a reptile? Explain your answer.

c)   The pigmy shrew is Britain's smallest mammal. It is only about 10 cm long including its tail. It can only survive in southern England. Suggest a reason for this.

7   Copy and correctly complete the statements below which are about the control of blood sugar levels. Choose words from the following list to fill in the blanks. (Each word may be used more than once if necessary.)

blood	**constant**	**glucose**	**hormone**	**insulin**	**liver**
lower/s	**pancreas**	**respiration**	**rise/s**	**diabetes**	

a)   The level of glucose sugar in the blood must be kept _____ if cells are to work properly. Glucose is continually removed from the blood by cells for use in _____. After a meal glucose levels in the blood _____.

b) When blood glucose levels are high the _____ secretes insulin into the _____. Insulin is a _____ which increases the permeability of body cells to _____ and causes the _____ to convert glucose into glycogen. This _____ the blood glucose levels.

c) If the blood glucose level is too low, no _____ is secreted. Glycogen stored in the liver is converted into _____ which passes into the blood.

d) The disease _____ is caused when the pancreas fails to produce insulin. The result is that the level of glucose in the blood _____.

8 The following questions are about diabetes:

a) One of the symptoms of diabetes is a feeling of severe thirst. Why does this happen?

b) Why do diabetics often carry chocolate or sweets with them wherever they go?

c) Why must insulin be injected rather than taken by mouth?

d) Try to find out which scientist/s

   i) discovered (in the 1920s) that the juice or extract from the pancreas could help sufferers from diabetes

   ii) worked out the chemical structure of insulin (in the 1950s)

e) Explain briefly how diabetics can now be provided with human insulin for injection.

9 a) Describe *three* ways in which water is important for the body.

b) Explain why the volume of water taken into the body must be balanced by the volume of water lost.

c) List *three* ways the body gains water and *four* ways the body loses water. Organise your answer in a table.

Water gain	Water loss

10 a) Make a *large* copy of the following diagram:

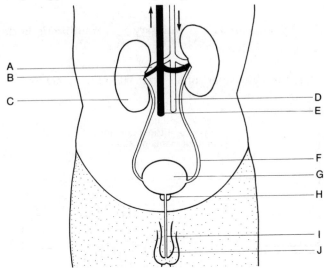

b) Write beside the letters A–J the correct labels chosen from the list below:

aorta   bladder   kidney   penis   renal artery   renal vein
ring of muscle   ureter   urethra   vena cava

Now make a list of the above labels and for each one choose the correct function from the list below:

i)   takes urine from the kidney to the bladder

ii)   prevents urine leaving the bladder

iii)   carries deoxygenated blood to the heart

iv)   removes urea from the blood

v)   carries urine out of the body

vi)   also used during sexual intercourse

vii)   carries blood to the kidney

viii) stores urine

ix)   carries blood away from the kidney

x)   brings oxygenated blood from the heart

11 a) Copy and complete this passage by choosing the correct word or words from inside the brackets:

After drinking several cups of tea or coffee the volume of the urine (increases/ decreases) and it looks (paler/yellower). The kidney is getting rid of excess (water/salt). On the other hand, on a hot day or after severe exercise the volume of urine (increases/decreases) and it looks (paler/yellower). This is called (excretion/osmoregulation).

b) Patients requiring dialysis by an artificial kidney machine must restrict their water and salt intake between dialysis sessions. Explain why.

12 Explain the role of each of the following in controlling the concentration of body fluids:

hypothalamus   **pituitary**   **antidiuretic hormone**

13 The diagram shows part of an artificial kidney machine.

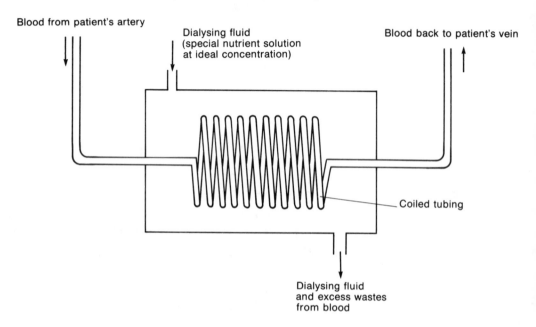

Blood from patient's artery

Dialysing fluid (special nutrient solution at ideal concentration)

Blood back to patient's vein

Coiled tubing

Dialysing fluid and excess wastes from blood

a) Why is the tubing coiled and not straight?

b) What material is the tubing likely to be made of?

c) What process causes excess water in the patient's blood to pass into the dialysing fluid?

d) i) Name an excretory product other than water which will pass out of the blood into the dialysing fluid.

ii) Where in the body is this excretory product made?

e) Why does this product pass from the blood in the coiled tubing into the dialysing fluid?

f) Name two nutrients present in the dialysing fluid.

g) Give two reasons why kidney transplantation is a better way of treating kidney failure than the use of a dialysis machine.

14 A manufacturer of the dialysis tubing used in artificial kidney machines has produced a new type of tubing. You are asked by the manufacturer to find out if the new tubing is permeable to urea at body temperature (37 °C). You are given:

ordinary laboratory apparatus
some of the new tubing
urea solution
a colourless dye which turns blue when mixed with urea

a) Make a large labelled diagram of the apparatus with solutions, set up ready for your experiment.

b) What result would show that urea can pass through the tubing?

15 Explain the difference between

a) excretion and egestion

b) urine and urea

c) homeostasis and homoiothermic

d) osmoregulation and thermoregulation

16 Read the passages below which are about the use of growth regulators in plants. Answer the questions which follow each one.

> The main function of plant hormones is to control growth. It is therefore hardly surprising that these hormones or similar chemicals made by Man, have been extensively used in crop production. Auxins are a group of hormones which have been isolated from a large number of different plants. **Synthetic auxins** are used as **selective weedkillers**. When sprayed onto crops they have a greater effect on broad-leaved plants than on the narrow-leaved ones. The growth of the broad-leaved plants is so severely disrupted that they die, while the narrow leaved plants at most suffer a temporary reduction in growth. As most of Man's cereal crops are narrow leaved and the weeds which compete with them are broad leaved, such selective weedkillers are extensively used. These weedkillers are also extensively used domestically to control weeds in lawns.
>
> Another synthetic auxin is used to increase fruit yield. When it is sprayed onto some species of fruit tree, it causes fruit to develop without the need for fertilisation. This is called **parthenocarpy**.
>
> Auxins are also the active ingredients of rooting powders. The development of roots is stimulated when the ends of cuttings are dipped into these compounds. Another plant hormone can be used to stimulate ripening of citrus fruits and tomatoes.

a) Explain what is meant by

   i) a synthetic auxin?

   ii) a selective weedkiller?

   iii) parthenocarpy?

b) Why do you think that selective weedkillers have a greater effect on broad-leaved plants?

c) Explain why selective weedkillers are used extensively by cereal farmers.

d) Why do gardeners use rooting powder?

One of the best known selective weedkillers is 2,4,5-trichlorophenoxyacetic acid (2,4,5-T). In its production an impurity called **dioxin** is formed. Dioxin is one of the most toxic substances known to Man, a single gram is enough to kill more than 5000 humans. Even in minute quantities it may cause cancer, a skin disorder called chloracne and abnormalities in unborn babies. Dioxin was a constituent of a **defolieant** called Agent Orange used by the Americans in the Vietnam war. Fifty million litres of it were sprayed over jungle areas to cause the leaves to drop so that enemy camps would be revealed. The dioxin produced physical and mental defects in children born in the area and to those born to American servicemen who were there when it was used. In 1976, an accident in Seveso, Italy, resulted in the release of dioxin into the atmosphere.

e) How is dioxin formed?

f) What is a 'defoliant'?

g) What conditions are likely to have been suffered by people who were living close to the factory at Seveso?

h) State one advantage and one disadvantage of using hormones to control growth in plants.

2.2.12 Healthy Living

1 The diagram below shows a vertical section through a human tooth.

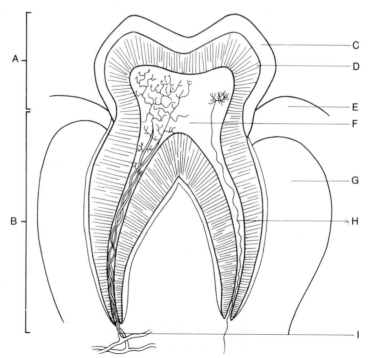

a) What is the name of this type of tooth?

b) Replace the letters A to I with the correct labels chosen from the list below:

   blood capillaries   crown   dentine   enamel   gum
   jawbone   nerve   pulp cavity   root

c) Study the diagram and complete the following sentences by filling in the missing word or words:

   i)   The part of the tooth which can be seen is called the _____.

   ii)   The _____ is embedded in the gum.

   iii) _____ is the hardest substance in the body.

   iv)   _____ forms the bulk of the tooth and decays easily.

   v)   The _____ contains the nerve and blood supply to the tooth.

d) Why do you think blood capillaries are present in the centre of the tooth?

2   The diagrams below show plans of teeth in the upper and lower jaw.

Plan A belongs to a 25-year-old man called Imran.
Plan B belongs to a 25-year-old man called Peter.

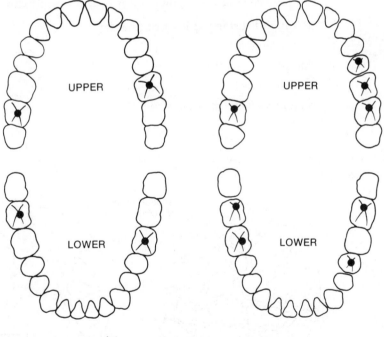

UPPER   UPPER

LOWER   LOWER

✖ Indicates decay has occurred

Plan A   Plan B

In the town where Imran lives the drinking water contains natural fluoride salts. There are no fluoride salts in the drinking water where Peter lives.

a) How many decayed teeth has

    i) Imran?

    ii) Peter?

b) What is the percentage of decayed teeth in

    i) Imran?

    ii) Peter?

c) Suggest *five* possible reasons why Peter has more decayed teeth than Imran.

d) Explain why it is the back teeth that have mostly decayed.

e) Some people believe that fluoride should not be added to drinking water. Why do you think this is?

3 a) What is plaque?

    b) Explain how bacteria in plaque can cause tooth decay.

    c) Why is it better to eat sweets at meal times rather than in between meals?

    d) What is periodontal disease and how is it caused?

    e) Explain how each of the following can help prevent tooth decay:

        i) thorough brushing at least once a day

        ii) use of dental floss

        iii) fluoride toothpaste

        iv) a sensible diet

        v) regular visits to the dentist

4 The diagram below shows microscopic sections of (A) healthy and (B) diseased lung tissue from adult humans.

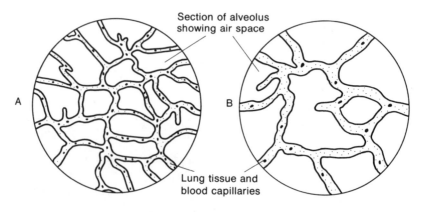

Section of alveolus showing air space

Lung tissue and blood capillaries

a)   What assumption must be made in order to compare the two sections?

b)   Give two structural differences between the healthy and the diseased lung which can be seen on the diagrams.

c)   Suggest for each difference you have described why it would make the diseased lung work less well.

d)   Give two possible causes of the lung damage.

5   Study the two graphs below, which show the effects of smoking on health.

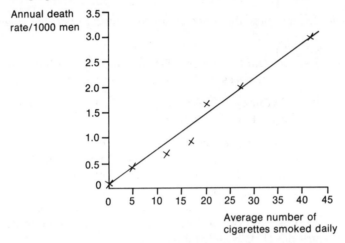

A   Death rate from lung cancer among men smoking different numbers of cigarettes each day

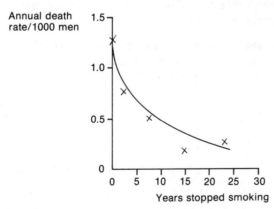

B   Death rate from lung cancer among men who gave up smoking cigarettes

a)   Out of a group of 5000 men smoking 30 cigarettes a day, how many are likely to die of lung cancer in one year?

b)   What effect does giving up smoking have on a man's chance of contracting lung cancer?

c)   Name *two* diseases other than lung cancer that can be caused by smoking.

d)   Why are pregnant women advised not to smoke?

6 a) Copy and complete this table about the constituents of cigarette smoke.

Constituent	Effect on the body
	Is addictive. It affects the nervous system, heart and blood vessels.
Tar	
	Anaesthetises cilia. It can combine with haemoglobin and reduce the ability of the blood to carry oxygen.

b) Explain how the lungs of smokers tend to become clogged up with mucus.

7 a) Use the words from this list to complete the following passage about heart disease. (If necessary you may use a word more than once.)

> atheroma   beating   blocked   coronary   death   fatty
> heart attack   oxygen

The heart muscle receives blood from the _____ arteries. If one of these vessels becomes _____ the heart muscle in that area stops _____ because it is being starved of nutrients and _____. This is called a _____. It often occurs quite suddenly and is a very common cause of _____. Many factors contribute to heart disease, although the blockage itself is often caused by _____ material deposited in the _____ arteries. This is called an _____.

b) Write a short leaflet entitled 'Looking after your Heart'. In it, mention each of the following factors:

> age   diet   smoking   excess alcohol consumption
> the need for physical exercise   stress   obesity
> high blood pressure

8 Which of the following best describes what a drug is?

a) a substance that harms the brain

b) a substance that helps the body to fight infection

c) a substance that is addictive

d) a substance that alters the way the body works

9 a) What is a medicine?

b) i)   What type of drug is aspirin?

ii) When is aspirin used as a medicine?

iii) What are the possible side effects of its use?

iv) Why should young children not be given aspirin?

10 Below are examples of drugs that affect the brain.

cannabis   alcohol   opium   nicotine   morphine
caffeine   barbiturates   sleeping pills   LSD   amphetamine
heroin   cocaine

a) Sort them into four groups under the following headings:

Sedative	Stimulant	Hallucinogen	Pain-killer

b) What is meant by drug abuse?

11 Read this passage about heroin addiction and then answer the following questions:

Heroin was originally developed medically as a pain-killer. It was used as a substitute for morphine in the belief that it was less likely to produce addiction. The opposite has proved to be true. Heroin is one of the most addictive of all drugs. It is taken in various ways; it can be sniffed or smoked, but generally it is injected. In the early stages the needle is inserted just under the skin ('skin-popping'). The user will then progress to intravenous injection ('main-lining') by which stage he or she will have developed into an addict.

Immediately after a dose of heroin the user experiences a state of sleepy well-being called euphoria. This fades quickly, passing into anxiety, agitation and constant worry about getting the next dose. With habitual use a heroin addict normally goes through successive stages of physical, mental and moral deterioration. The way of life of many addicts is characterised by personal neglect – irregular and insufficient meals, insanitary habits and a disregard for hygienic precautions during injections. Infections are common e.g. abscesses and hepatitis. This neglect frequently leads to an early death. The suicide rate among heroin addicts is said to be fifty times greater than it is in the general population. An addict who becomes pregnant may pass on the addiction to her baby. Immediate removal of the drug causes violent withdrawal symptoms which include sweating, convulsions, vomiting and diarrhoea. This is a painful and terrifying experience.

a) Why is it not desirable to use heroin medically as a pain-killer?

b) Briefly explain the following terms:

addiction   euphoria   withdrawal symptoms

c) What is the difference between 'skin-popping' (line 5) and 'main-lining' (line 6)?

d) What is meant by 'physical, mental and moral deterioration' (line 11)?

e) What hygienic precautions should normally be taken before an injection?

f) What factors contribute to the early death of heroin addicts?

g) Why is widthdrawal sickness known among addicts as 'the horrors'?

h) Addicts do not usually get pregnant because regular heroin injections tend to stop menstruation. Why might this be considered a fortunate effect?

i) Why do you think AIDS has spread very rapidly amongst intravenous drug users?

12 Name a disease

   a) which is infectious

   b) which is inherited

   c) which is caused by a poor diet

   d) which is caused by harmful chemicals

   e) whose cause is unknown

   f) which is transmitted only by sexual intercourse

13 Choose one disease caused by each of the following organisms:

     a bacterium   **a virus**   **a fungus**   **a protist**

Record information about each disease by copying the following table and filling in the spaces:

Name of disease	Caused by	Main symptoms	Spread by
	A bacterium		
	A virus		
	A fungus		
	A protist		

14 Write a short account of how the skin and white blood cells help to protect us against harmful microbes.

15 Read this passage and answer the questions which follow about Jenner's discovery of vaccination.

> Edward Jenner first used vaccination at the end of the eighteenth century. Girls who milked cows caught a mild disease called cowpox. After they had had cowpox, they did not seem to catch smallpox. Jenner carried out an experiment. He obtained some pus from a scab on the hand of a dairymaid with cowpox. He then scratched some of the pus into the arm of an eight-year-old boy called James Phipps. The boy caught cowpox but soon recovered. Jenner then transferred pus from a smallpox victim to James. James did not catch smallpox.

   a) What observation led Jenner to make his discovery?

   b) Describe the experiment Jenner carried out.

c)   What would most likely have happened to James Phipps if Jenner's experiment had not worked? What would have happened to Jenner in that case?

d)   Why was Jenner's discovery so important?

e)   Jenner called his method of protecting people against smallpox 'vaccination'. Choose two words from the list which are often used nowadays instead of 'vaccination':

   infusion   inoculation   injection   immunisation

f)   Why are people no longer vaccinated against smallpox?

16   a)   If a person is 'immune' to a disease what does this mean?

b)   Explain two ways in which it is possible to become immune to measles.

c)   Here is a brief outline of immunisation. Use it to write a complete paragraph called 'How immunisation works'.

   A small weak dose of microbes is injected or given by mouth.
   Microbes multiply inside the body.
   Antibodies are made.
   Microbes are destroyed by the antibodies.
   Antibodies remain in the blood.
   Booster doses of vaccine are given. More antibodies are made.
   Antibodies protect against the disease for several years.

d)   i)   Name *three* diseases against which babies are immunised and *one* disease against which teenagers are immunised.

   ii) Name *one* disease against which you cannot be immunised.

   iii) Why is it important that girls are immunised against German measles (rubella) in their early teens?

17   Read the two passages a) and b) and answer the questions on each passage.

a)   In 1928 Professor Alexander Fleming discovered that a **mould** found growing on a **bacterial plate** produced a substance that killed the bacteria on the plate. He went on to find out that this substance produced by the mould had the power of destroying all kinds of bacteria that cause human disease. He identified the mould as *Penicillium notatum*.
      Fleming injected his **bacteriocidal** substance into mice and found that it did them no harm. However he also found that the substance lost its power to kill bacteria if kept for any length of time.

   i)   Explain the following:

   mould   bacterial plate   bacteriocidal

   ii) What name was given to the substance produced by the mould?

   iii) Try to find out more about how Alexander Fleming made his discovery.

b)   Surprisingly, there was very little interest in Fleming's discovery. It was not until 1938 that two scientists from Oxford called Florey and Chain repeated Fleming's experiments. They obtained the same results and also showed that the substance could kill harmful bacteria which had been injected into mice.

Most of their tests were completed by 1940, and because it was now wartime there was an urgent need for such a drug. Many scientists worked to find a way of making and preserving it in a new pure form. Eventually they succeeded and it began to be made commercially.

i)   Why is it surprising that there was no interest in Fleming's discovery for ten years?

ii) How might Florey and Chain have shown that 'the substance could kill harmful bacteria which had been injected into mice'?

iii) Why was there an urgent need in wartime for a drug with the power to kill bacteria?

iv) What name is given to all substances that are produced by microbes and have the power to kill bacteria?

v)   Give another example of such a substance.

vi) Name *two* diseases that can now be easily cured by these drugs but would probably have caused death 60 years ago.

18 Substance X is extracted from a living organism. The diagram below shows the effect it has on bacteria growing on agar jelly. Disc A has been soaked in a high concentration of X; disc B has been soaked in a low concentrtion of X; disc C was soaked in distilled water only. The three discs were placed on the surface of the agar jelly using sterile forceps. Bacteria had already been introduced into the agar jelly. The agar plate with the three discs in position was incubated **for** eighteen hours at 37 °C.

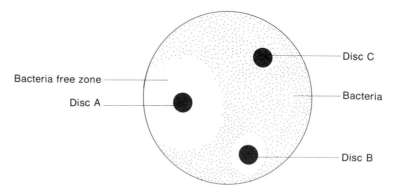

a)   Why was disc C included in the experiment?

b)   What effect does X appear to have on bacterial growth?

c)   By what process would substance X get into the agar?

d)   What is the general name given to a substance such as X?

e)   Name one specific example of a substance that has properties similar to X's.

19 Study the diagram below of a particularly disgusting grocer's shop and its staff toilet.

If you were a Public Health Inspector, what changes would you insist on in order to make this shop more hygienic?

20 Syphilis and gonorrhoea are two forms of sexually transmitted diseases.

a) How are each of these diseases spread?

b) What are the early symptoms of syphilis in

   i) the male?

   ii) the female?

    c) What are the early symptoms of gonorrhoea in

        i)   the male?

        ii) the female?

    d) What happens if gonorrhoea is not treated?

    e) What type of disease organism causes

        i)   syphilis?

        ii) gonorrhoea?

    f) How can the spread of the two diseases be prevented?

21 Copy and complete this passage about the Acquired Immune Deficiency Syndrome (AIDS). Fill in the gaps with words from the following list. (If necessary you may use a word more than once.)

> skin   placenta   sexual   lungs   immune
> Human Immunodeficiency Virus   blood   pneumonia
> lymphocytes   chicken pox   AIDS   milk   needles

    a) AIDS is caused by a virus called the _____ . In humans this virus attacks and destroys _____ . These cells help to protect us from diseases, such as _____ and _____ .

        People with a damaged _____ system are more likely to suffer from one or more of such diseases. People do not die of _____ . They die from diseases which their bodies can no longer fight. The _____ , _____ and brain are most commonly infected.

        AIDS is usually transmitted by intimate _____ contact, or when the _____ of an infected person mixes with the _____ of someone else. It is readily transmitted among drug addicts who share _____ to inject themselves. An infected mother can pass AIDS onto her baby, either across the _____ during pregnancy or later in the _____ during breast feeding.

        Now answer these questions.

    b) What is meant by a high risk group when referring to AIDS?

    c) Which people are considered to be in these high risk groups and why?

    d) What precautions can be taken to restrict the spread of AIDS?

    e) Many scientists are predicting that a vaccine will not be available until at least the year 2000.

        Why does it take so long to develop such a vaccine?

2.3 GENETICS AND EVOLUTION

2.3.1 Variation

1 The drawings below are of two arthropod animals, of different species, which live on the sea shore.

    a) Look carefully at the two drawings and describe *four similarities* and *four differences* that you can see between the two animals. Record your observations in a table.

    b) Suggest *two ways* in which animal B is adapted to its way of life.

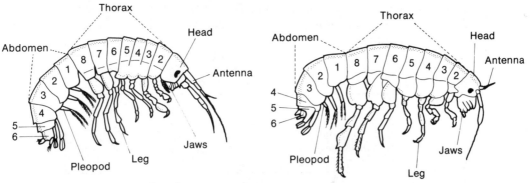

Animal A swims in rock pools   Animal B lives in burrows above high tide mark

2 Copy and complete these sentences by choosing the correct word from inside the brackets:

    a) Offspring produced by asexual reproduction are always (different/identical) and so there is (no/much) variation.

    b) Offspring produced by sexual reproduction are always (different/identical) and so there is (no/much) variation.

3 a) List *three* ways in which all humans are alike.

    b) List *three* ways in which humans vary.

4 a) Decide which of the statements below apply to identical twins and which ones apply to non-identical twins:

       i)   They are formed from a single fertilised egg which splits into two.

       ii)   They are formed from two separate eggs, fertilised by two separate sperms.

       iii)   They each have their own placenta.

       iv)   They share the same placenta.

     v)   They are always the same sex.

     vi)   They may be of the same sex or different sexes.

     vii) They are also known as fraternal twins.

     viii) They each have the same genes.

     ix)   They are only as alike as any brothers and sisters.

     x)   They sometimes develop as Siamese twins.

  b) Draw diagrams to show how identical and non-identical twins are produced.

5 Studying twins which have been brought up together and apart has helped to work out whether variations are controlled by genes inherited from parents, or by the environment. Explain why studying twins is so useful in this type of research.

6 The information given in the tables below was obtained from studies of twins. The figures show the average *differences* in certain characteristics between pairs of twins. The results were obtained from two different studies. Look carefully at the information in the table and answer the questions which follow.

Average difference in:	Identical twins reared together	Identical twins reared apart
Height/cm	1.7	1.8
Mass/kg	1.9	4.5
Head length/mm	2.9	2.2
Head width/mm	2.8	2.85
IQ	3.1	6.0

  a) Which of the characteristics remain almost the same even when the twins were brought up in different homes? What does this tell you about these characteristics?

  b) Which of the characteristics change when the twins are brought up in different homes? Suggest an explanation for this.

  c) Why is it difficult to collect data such as this?

7 The following information about height and blood groups was obtained from a group of 20 students.

Height/cm	Blood group	Height/cm	Blood group
164	O	179	A
172	AB	176	A
169	B	171	O
172	A	178	O
166	O	184	AB
158	A	187	O
183	B	177	B
169	A	178	O
181	O	174	O
173	A	176	B

a) Arrange this information into classes for height and blood group. To do this copy and complete the tables below.

i)

Height/cm	156–160	161–165	166–170	171–175	176–180	181–185	186–190
Number of students							

ii)

Blood group	A	AB	O	B
Number of students				

b) i) Draw a histogram to illustrate the variation in height in the group of students.

   ii) Is height an example of **continuous** or **discontinuous** variation?

c) i) Draw a bar chart to illustrate the variation in blood group.

   ii) Is blood grouping an example of **continuous** or **discontinuous** variation?

d) Explain the difference between continuous and discontinuous variation.

e) List *three* examples of continuous variation and *three* examples of discontinuous variation in humans.

2.3.2 Chromosomes

1 Choose words from this list to fill in the gaps in the passage below:

7	23	46	127	nucleus	genes	homologous
inheritance		divide	numbér	pairs	staining	gene

Chromosomes are found in the _____ of every living cell. They can be seen by _____ a cell that is about to _____. For each thread-like chromosome there is another one exactly like it; therefore chromosomes occur in _____. Every body cell of a particular organism has the same _____ of chromosomes. For example, all humans have _____ chromosomes in each body cell, made up of _____ pairs. The cells of the garden pea have 14 chromosomes made up of _____ pairs and those of the shrimp have 254 chromsomes, made up of _____ pairs. The two chromosomes belonging to a matching pair are called _____ chromosomes.

Each chromosome contains a large number of _____. Each _____ determines the _____ of a particular characteristic.

2 When organisms grow they increase the number of cells they are made of. A single cell divides to form two cells. The two new cells must have chromosomes that are identical to those of the original cell from which they were formed. In this way all the cells of an organism will have a set of chromosomes identical to that of the single fertilised egg from which they grew.

a) Copy and complete the diagram below by drawing in the nuclei of the two cells produced when the original cell divides during growth and asexual reproduction.

A cell of an imaginary organism with four chromosomes

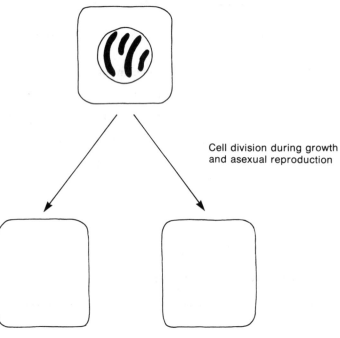

Cell division during growth and asexual reproduction

Two daughter cells

b) What name is given to this type of cell division?

3 a) If a human egg and a human sperm each carried 46 chromosomes, how many chromosomes would there be in the fertilised egg?

b) How many chromosomes would there be in all the cells of the baby which grew from the fertilised egg?

c) How many chromosomes must there be in human eggs and sperms to prevent the doubling of the chromosome number?

4 In the formation of reproductive cells (gametes), a special type of cell division occurs which halves the number of chromosomes.

a) Copy and complete the diagram below by drawing in the nuclei of the four cells produced when the original cell divides to form reproductive cells.

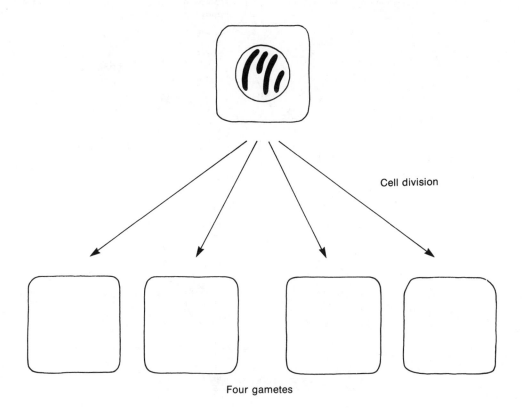

Cell division

Four gametes

b) What name is given to this type of cell division?

c) Where does it occur in

   i) a mammal?

   ii) a flowering plant?

d) Explain why it is necessary for reproductive cells to be formed in this way.

e) Copy and complete this sentence:
   The nuclei of reproductive cells or _____ contain only _____ member of each pair of _____ chromsomes.

5 In this diagram of the human life cycle the circles represent the cells.

a) Copy and complete the diagram below by writing in the circles the numbers of chromosomes found in those cells.

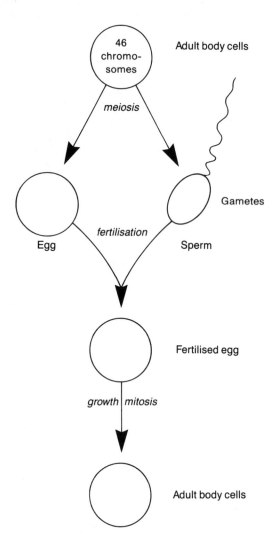

b) Which of the cells in the diagram are **diploid** (have the full number of chromosomes) and which are **haploid** (have only half the full number)?

6 a) What are **sex chromosomes**?

b) How do human males and females differ in their sex chromosomes?

c) How many sex chromosomes are found in a gamete?

d) The diagram below shows the sex chromosomes of a human couple, four of their children and the gametes from which these children began.

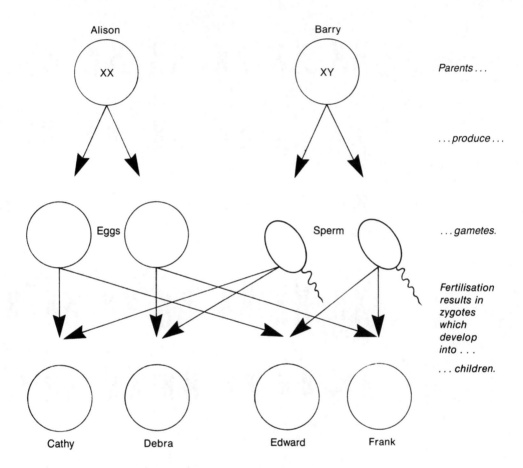

i) Copy the diagram and fill in the sex chromosomes of the gametes and children.

ii) Is it the egg nucleus or the sperm nucleus which determines the sex of the baby?

iii) If another child was expected, what would be its chance of being a boy?

iv) From which parent would the boy inherit a Y chromosome?

7 The diagrams show the chromosomes of two different children.

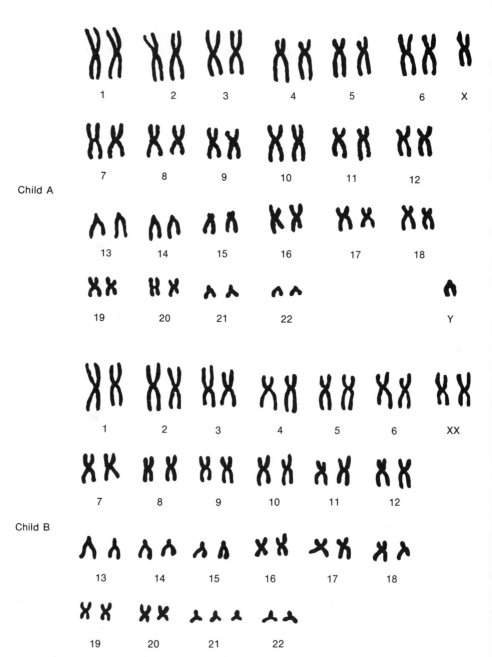

Child A

Child B

a) Study the diagrams and give *two* differences between child A and child B.

b) Which child has an abnormal set of chromosomes?

c) What is the name of the genetic disorder caused by the abnormality?

d) It is possible to detect this abnormality in an unborn baby by the process of amniocentesis.

    i)   What does this process involve?

    ii) What is the advantage of detecting abnormalities in an unborn child?

    iii) Research has been carried out into ways of detecting abnormalities in the first few weeks of pregnancy. What is the advantage of this?

2.3.3 Patterns of Inheritance

1 Use the word 'inheritance' (or 'inherited') in a sentence which shows that you understand its meaning.

2 Read the passage below and then answer the following questions.

> Gregor Mendel carried out experiments with pea plants. In one experiment he studied how the height of the pea plant was inherited. He took **pure-breeding** tall plants and crossed them with **pure-breeding** dwarf plants. He collected the pea seeds that were produced and grew them to produce the F_1 generation. All the F_1 plants were tall.
>
> He then allowed the F_1 tall plants to self-fertilise. He collected the seeds and grew them to produce the F_2 generation. Three-quarters of these plants were tall, and one-quarter were dwarf.

a) Who was Gregor Mendel? When and where did he live?

b) If pure-breeding tall plants are self-fertilised what kind of plants will always grow from the seeds that are produced?

c) Which characteristic is dominant, tall or dwarf? How do you know this?

d) Did Mendel know about genes when he did his work?

e) How many genes that control the height of the plants are found in each cell of the pea plants?

f) How many genes for height are found in a pollen grain nucleus or egg cell?

g) Let the gene for tallness $= T$; let the gene for dwarfism $= t$. Copy and complete this diagram to show the genes present in the gametes and F_1 plants.

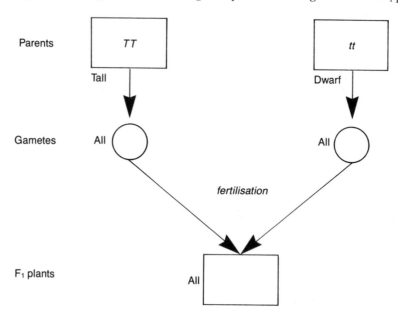

h) Copy this diagram, which shows the cross between the F_1 plants, and complete it by writing in the boxes the genes of the parents and the F_2 plants.

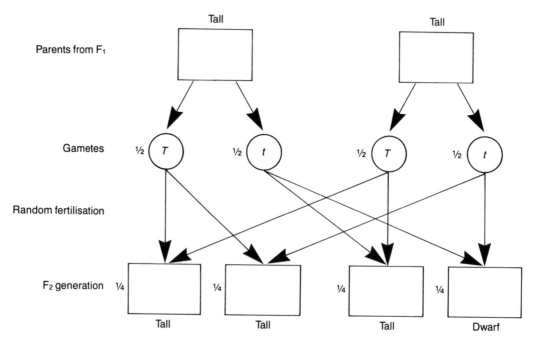

i) Why is a capital letter used to represent the gene for tallness and a small letter used for the gene for dwarfism?

3 Pea plants are normally self-pollinated. How did Mendel cross-pollinate the flowers in his experiments?

4 What are the *four* basic rules of **genetics** first discovered by Mendel?

5 a) What are homologous chromosomes?

b) Homologous chromosomes have genes for the same characteristic in the same position. *Tall* and *dwarf* are different forms of the gene for the characteristic of stem length in pea plants.

   i) Draw a pair of homologous chromosomes.

   ii) Mark the position of the gene T for tall stem at any point on one of the chromosomes.

   iii) Mark the position of the gene t for dwarf stem on the other chromosome.

c) Try to explain why gametes only carry one gene for each characteristic whereas body cells carry two.

6 Match the words in the left-hand column with the definitions in the right-hand column.

Words	Definitions
a) **phenotype**	different forms of the gene for the same characteristic
b) **genotype**	the allele which has an effect in either the homozygous or heterozygous condition
c) **homozygous**	the genes that an organism contains
d) **heterozygous**	the allele which only has an effect when homozygous.
e) **alleles**	having two identical genes for a particular characteristic
f) **dominant**	an organism's outward appearance
g) **recessive**	having two different genes for a particular characteristic

7 Copy and complete these sentences by choosing the correct word from inside the brackets:

a) A pea plant whose (genotype/phenotype) is tall could have the (genotype/phenotype) TT or Tt.

b) A tall pea plant with genotype TT is (homozygous/heterozygous) dominant.

c) A tall pea plant with genotype *Tt* is (homozygous/heterozygous) dominant.

d) A dwarf pea plant with genotype *tt* is (homozygous/heterozygous) recessive.

e) *T* and *t* are both (alleles/chromosomes) of the gene for stem length.

In any of the following questions, if the word **allele** *confuses you replace it with the word* **gene**.

8 In humans the ability to roll the tongue is caused by a dominant allele. The family tree below shows the inheritance of tongue rolling ability in a family.

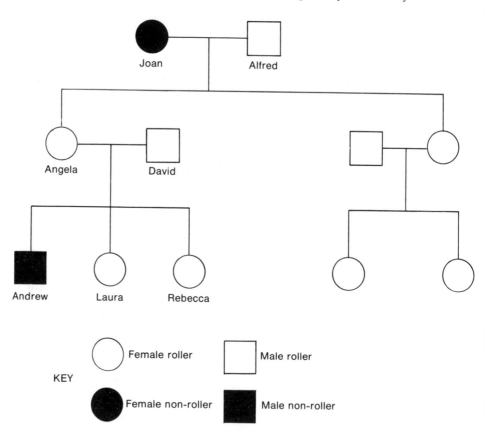

a) How many alleles for non-rolling must Andrew have inherited?

b) Which of Andrew's parents must carry the non-rolling allele?

c) From which of his grandparents did Andrew inherit the allele for non-rolling?

d) i) Copy the family tree.

ii) Using R to represent the allele for rolling and r for the non-rolling allele, show on your diagram the genotypes of Joan, Angela, David and Andrew.

iii) What are the possible genotypes of Alfred, Laura and Rebecca?

9 In mice, the coat colour black is dominant over the coat colour brown. Let the allele for black coat = B and the allele for brown coat = b.

a) Explain, with the help of a diagram, how two black mice could produce a brown offspring.

b) If you had a black mouse, how could you prove that it was carrying the allele for brown coat colour i.e. that it was heterozygous Bb?

10 Choose words from the list below to complete the following sentences. Each word can be used once, more than once or not at all.

allele   cells   chromosome   dominant   gametes   gene
mutant   mutation   one   recessive   two

a) A change in a gene or a chromosome is called a _____.

b) Mutation can result in the formation of a new _____ for a particular characteristic.

c) In order to be passed on to the next generation, mutations must occur in cells from which _____ are formed, or in the _____ themselves.

d) Down's syndrome is caused by a _____ mutation. People with Down's syndrome have _____ extra _____.

e) Most mutations produce _____ alleles and only show up if identical mutant alleles happen to occur in the same person.

f) Albinism is caused by a mutation in the _____ for the production of skin pigments.

11 Mutations occur constantly in populations. However it is possible to increase the rate at which mutations occur.

List *four* agents which can cause mutations.

12 Read this passage which is about an **inherited disease**, and then answer the following questions.

Cystic fibrosis is an inherited disease caused by a recessive allele which is a mutant form of the normal allele found in healthy people. Children with this disease produce very sticky mucus which clogs the lungs and intestines. This leads to infection and serious tissue damage. Before the introduction of antibiotics most sufferers died in infancy due to constant infections. Drugs are now available which are inhaled as a vapour and soften the mucus helping to prevent infection. Cystic fibrosis also makes sweat more salty. Simple tests on sweat can help to detect the disease in infancy and allow doctors to start treatment before irreversible lung damage has been done.

a) Explain the meaning of the following as used in the first sentence of the passage:

   i)   an inherited disease

   ii) a recessive allele

   iii) a mutant form of the normal allele

b) Why did the introduction of antibiotics help to prolong the life of cystic fibrosis sufferers?

c) Why would salty sweat pose a greater problem to sufferers in a hot country than in Britain?

d) What is the advantage of detecting the disease early?

e) Name *two* other diseases that are inherited and *two* diseases that are not inherited.

13 The family tree below shows the inheritance of cystic fibrosis in one family.

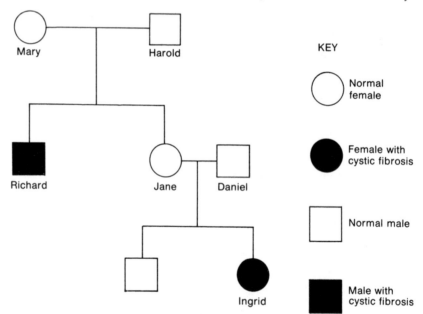

a) Select symbols to represent the normal and cystic fibrosis alleles.

b) Give the **genotypes** of each of the people named in the family.

c) What are the possible genotypes of the son of Jane and Daniel?

d) If Jane and Daniel have another child what is the probability of its being

   i)   completely normal

   ii) a sufferer from cystic fibrosis

   iii) a carrier of the disease?

e) After the discovery that Ingrid had cystic fibrosis, Jane and Daniel went to see a genetic counsellor. What would have been the purpose of such a visit?

14 a) How many alleles has the gene for ABO blood grouping in humans?

b) How many alleles for this are carried by each person?

c) Copy and complete this table.

Blood group (phenotype)	Possible genotypes
A B AB O	

d) The alleles A and B are co-dominant. What does this mean?

e) It is possible for all four blood groups to occur in the children of one family. Write a full genetic explanation of how this could happen.

f) A woman of blood group A claims that a man of blood group AB is the father of her child who is group O. Is this possible? Write out a full explanation of your answer.
Could he have been the father if he had been group B?

15 In Shorthorn cattle the alleles for coat colour are co-dominant. If a red cow is crossed with a white bull the calves all have a mixture of red and white hairs and are called **roans**. (The same happens with a white cow and a red bull.)

What are the possible coat colours in the offspring produced from crossing a roan cow and a roan bull? Write out a full explanation of your answer.

2.3.4 More about Genes

1 Copy and complete this paragraph about **DNA**.

Chromosomes are made up of DNA. DNA is short for _____. It carries the coded instructions for how an organism will develop. The instructions control the synthesis of _____ in the cell. A length of DNA which codes for one protein is called a _____. Most of the proteins produced by a cell are _____. The DNA molecule is made up of two strands twisted together into a spiral or double _____. Untwisted the molecule is like a _____ whose rungs are made up of pairs of organic _____. There are _____ different bases.

2 a) The bases of DNA are known by their initial letters. What does each letter stand for?

    i) A =

    ii) C =

    iii) T =

    iv) G =

  b) The diagram below shows a small part of a DNA molecule. The bases are labelled only on one strand. Copy the diagram and label all the bases.

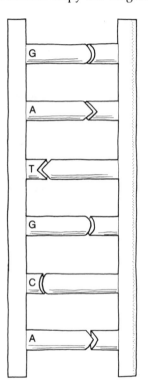

3 Copy and complete these sentences.

  a) A protein is a long chain of _____ in a specific sequence. There are _____ different amino acids.

  b) A _____ is a row of three bases on a DNA strand. It codes for one _____.

  c) Protein synthesis occurs in structures in the cytoplasm called _____.

  d) A molecule called _____ RNA is a copy of a portion of _____. It carries genetic information from the nucleus to the _____.

  e) The order of _____ in the m RNA controls the order of _____ in a protein molecule.

4 a) Why is it necessary for DNA to be able to replicate accurately?

b) Explain why each of the following properties of DNA make accurate replication possible:

    i)   The hydrogen bonds between the bases are easily broken.

    ii) Adenine can only pair with thymine and cytosine with guanine.

5 Read this passage which is about **genetic engineering** and then answer the following questions:

> Genetic engineering uses techniques that allow scientists to transfer genes from one organism to another. Simple, rapidly reproducing organisms like bacteria can be used as chemical factories for making substances needed by other organisms, such as humans. An example is insulin.
>
> Many people suffer from a disease called diabetes, which means that they cannot make the hormone insulin. In healthy people it is produced after a meal and instructs the tissues to absorb glucose from the blood. Many diabetics inject insulin, taken from animals, into their bodies to replace the insulin they cannot make themselves. However, animal insulin differs slightly from the human variety and sometimes has unpleasant side effects.
>
> Scientists now use genetic engineering to produce human insulin. They can transfer the insulin gene from human cells to a bacterium by using special enzymes. The bacterium reproduces rapidly, soon producing millions of bacterial cells, all able to make human insulin. Bacteria can be grown in huge numbers in large vats like those used for brewing beer. Therefore in the future the use of human insulin produced by bacteria should be common.
>
> Another disease that some people have stops them from producing growth hormone in their pituitary glands. Unfortunately only human growth hormone can be used to treat these people. Until recently this could only be obtained from pituitary glands taken from corpses. Very large numbers of pituitary glands are needed to treat one individual. Genetic engineering techniques have now been developed that enable human growth hormone to be produced by bacteria.

a) Which organ of the body produces insulin?

b) What is the effect on the body of a deficiency of insulin?

c) Why is insulin from animals not as desirable for treating diabetics as human insulin?

d) Why is it significant that bacteria

    i)   reproduce very rapidly?

    ii) can be grown in huge numbers in large vats?

e) What is the effect on the body of a deficiency of growth hormone?

f) Explain how genetic engineering could be used to produce human growth hormone.

6   Biologists have managed to change the genes in larger animals like mice. The diagram below shows how giant mice have been bred by genetic engineering. Study the diagram and answer the questions below.

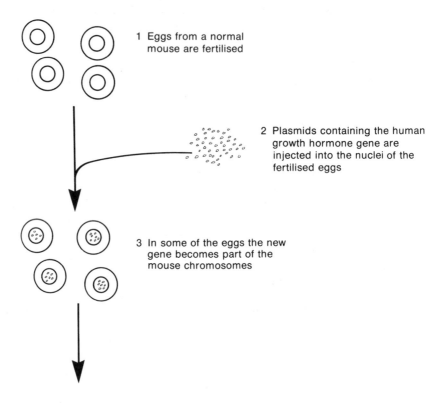

1 Eggs from a normal mouse are fertilised

2 Plasmids containing the human growth hormone gene are injected into the nuclei of the fertilised eggs

3 In some of the eggs the new gene becomes part of the mouse chromosomes

4 The eggs are put back into a female mouse and allowed to develop

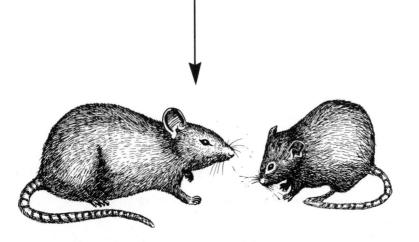

5 Some of the mice produced from these eggs grow to be giant mice

a) How would the mice eggs have been fertilised?

b) What are plasmids?

c) Which human gene has been inserted into the plasmids?

d) What caused some of the baby mice to grow up to 25% bigger than their parents?

e) Would you expect the offspring of these giant mice to be normal or giant? Explain why.

f) Should biologists be allowed to carry out this kind of experiment? What are the possible consequences of such research?

7 Read the passage below which is about cloning plants. Answer the questions which follow.

> A group of **genetically identical** individuals is called a clone. Asexual methods of reproduction in plants produce offspring which come from the same parent and belong to the same clone. Some plants can be successfully cloned from single cells of the parent plant by a technique called tissue culture. This relies on the fact that all body cells of an individual carry the same genetic information. Carrot plants were the first to be cloned in this way. Using **sterile techniques** a tiny piece of stem is cut from a carrot seedling. This is put onto **nutrient agar** in a petri dish. The cells of the stem **divide mitotically** to form a clump of cells called a callus. These cells can be separated and each one grown into a new carrot plant.
>
> Much research is being carried out into cloning economically important plants. **High yielding** varieties of the oil palm (used in the production of margarine, soaps and detergents) have been successfully cloned but it took scientists at Unilever ten years to develop the tissue culture techniques required. The possibility of cloning Norway Spruce trees which are resistant to acid rain is being investigated.

a) Explain the meaning of each of the following as used in the passage:
   i)   genetically identical
   ii) sterile techniques
   iii) nutrient agar
   iv) divide mitotically
   v)   high yielding

b) Describe two methods of cloning plants without using tissue culture.

c) Explain why the carrot plants, produced by the method described in the passage, form a clone.

d) Oil palms can be grown from the seeds collected from high yielding varieties. Why do you think Unilever spent so long looking for a way to clone the plants?

e) Why are Norway Spruce trees of economic importance?

2.3.5 Evolution

1 a) What were the earliest forms of life on Earth, small simple organisms or large complex ones?

   b) Where were the earliest forms of life to be found?

   c) What is meant by evolution?

   d) Try to find out how many millions of years ago scientists believe that

   i)   the Earth was formed

   ii)   the first life evolved

   iii) the dinosaurs died out

   iv) modern Man appeared

2 Fossils provide us with evidence for evolution.

   a) What are fossils?

   b) Describe *two* ways in which fossils are formed.

   c) What evidence is there from fossils to suggest that reptiles lived before mammals?

3 Today, most scientists accept the theories of evolution first put forward by Charles Darwin in 1858. Use reference books to find out about Darwin and answer the following questions:

   a) Before the 19th century, how did people believe that new species came about? (Some people still believe this today.)

   b) When was Darwin born?

   c) What was the name of the ship on which he sailed to South America in 1832?

   d) How long did the voyage last?

   e) Which islands did Darwin visit and where are they?

   f) What did he find particularly interesting about the wildlife on these islands?

   g) How long after his return to England did Darwin publish his theory? Why do you think it took him so long?

   h) Who was the scientist who independently came to the same conclusions as Darwin?

   i) What was the title of the book published by Darwin in 1859?

   j) Were Darwin's theories immediately accepted?

4 Darwin observed that most organisms produce large numbers of young. However, he also noticed that populations do not generally increase rapidly in size, but stay more or less constant.

How did he explain this?

5 Jean-Baptiste Lamarck (1744–1829) was a French biologist who put forward a theory of evolutionary change before that of Darwin. He explained the evolution of the giraffe's long neck in the following way:

> Ancestors of the present giraffe aquired a slightly longer neck by stretching to reach leaves high up in the trees. The offspring of these giraffes inherited this longer neck. These offspring, in reaching for food, stretched their necks more and their offspring inherited the even longer necks. This continued over many generations until the present long neck was aquired.

How would Darwin's theory explain the giraffe's long neck?

6 Explain how natural selection has been involved in *one* of the following situations:

a) The peppered moth exists in two forms, pale and dark. In industrial areas the dark variety is more common. In country areas the pale variety is the more common.

b) There are some types of bacteria that were once killed by penicillin, but are now resistant to it.

c) New types of mosquito have arisen which are resistant to DDT.

d) Rats are normally killed by a poison called warfarin, but the number of rats that are not affected by the poison is on the increase.

7 Read this passage, which is about selective breeding, and answer the questions which follow.

> Man has cultivated plants and kept animals for about 10 000 years. Over this time he has bred them selectively to produce desirable characteristics. For example, modern varieties of cattle have been bred over a very long time to give a high milk yield or fast meat production. From the varied individuals among a herd of cattle, breeders choose only those with desirable characteristics to breed and produce the next generation. Plant breeders have bred varieties of wheat and rice which grow more quickly, give a higher yield of grain and are more resistant to disease.
>
> However, the varieties of animals and plants which have been specially bred by Man, would very often be unable to survive in the wild. Some farmers are now beginning to think differently about the characteristics they want in their animals and plants. Instead of enormous yields, they are now looking for varieties of crops that can grow well with less fertilisers or pesticides and varieties of animals that require less expensive housing and food. Luckily many of the older breeds which have these desirable characteristics have been conserved. These can be used in breeding programmes to develop new varieties.

a) What is meant by 'selective breeding'?

b) What are the advantages to Man of breeding new varieties of food crops such as wheat and rice?

c) According to the passage, what characteristics might be developed by plant and animal breeders in the future?

d) Why is it important to conserve the older varieties of animals and plants?

8 Read this passage and answer the questions which follow it. The passage is about the evolution of bread wheat and is adapted from *The Ascent of Man* by J. Bronowski.

> The turning point in the spread of agriculture was almost certainly the occurence of two forms of wheat with a large, full head of seeds. Before 8000 BC wheat was not the luxuriant plant it is today; it was merely one of many wild grasses that spread throughout the Middle East. By some genetic accident, the wild wheat crossed with a natural goat grass and formed a fertile hybrid. The fourteen chromosomes of wild wheat were combined with the fourteen chromosomes of goat grass, and produced Emmer with twenty-eight chromosomes. The seeds of Emmer wheat were much plumper than the wild wheat and were attached to the husk in such a way that they scattered in the wind. For such a hybrid to be fertile is rare but not unique among plants.
>
> There was a second genetic accident in which Emmer crossed with another natural goat grass and produced a still larger hybrid with forty-two chromosomes which is bread wheat. However this wheat can only be propagated by man. The seeds will never spread in the wind because the ear is too tight to break up. The life of each, man and plant, depends on the other. It is a true fairy tale of genetics – as if the coming of civilisation had been blessed in advance by the spirit of the abbot Gregor Mendel.

a) Why was the occurrence of wheat with a large full head of seeds a 'turning point' to the spread of agriculture?

b) Consider a plant with a chromosome number of fourteen.

i) How many chromosomes would you normally expect to find in the gametes of this plant?

ii) What would you expect to be the chromosome number of the offspring grown from a seed of this plant?

c) Why is the crossing of wild wheat with a natural goat grass described as a genetic accident?

d) What is a hybrid?

e) Why would bread wheat not survive in the wild?

TOPIC 3

Materials Science

3.1   Types and Uses of Materials
3.1.1 Solids, Liquids and Gases
3.1.2 Elements, Compounds and Mixtures
3.1.3 The Periodic Table
3.1.4 Acids, Alkalis and Salts
3.1.5 Petrochemicals
3.1.6 More Chemicals in our Lives
3.2   Making New Materials
3.2.1 Classifying Change
3.2.2 Chemicals of Life
3.2.3 Chemical Reactions and Energy Transfer
3.2.4 Rate of Reaction
3.2.5 Industrial Processes
3.3   Explaining How Materials Behave
3.3.1 Particles and Matter
3.3.2 Formulae and Equations
3.3.3 Chemical Calculations
3.3.4 Structure and Bonding
3.3.5 Ions and Electrolysis
3.3.6 Radioactivity

3.1 TYPES AND USES OF MATERIALS

3.1.1 Solids, Liquids and Gases

1   Copy and complete the diagram below by adding the *reverse process* for each of those labelled.

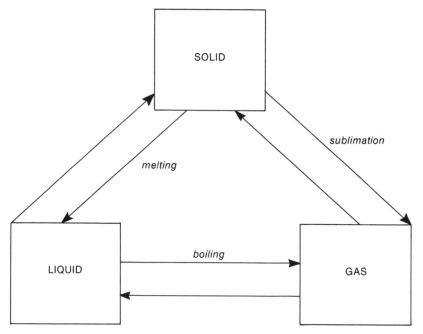

2   This packet of sugar claims that it is 'quick dissolving':

a)   What is likely to be different about the sugar in the packet, compared to ordinary sugar, which makes it quick dissolving?

b)   Design an experiment to test whether or not the sugar does dissolve quicker than ordinary sugar. List the apparatus you would use, what you would do, and how you would make sure the comparison was fair.

3 Explain why 10 g zinc powder reacts more quickly with dilute acid than a single zinc granule of the same mass.

4 You have been given the following equipment:

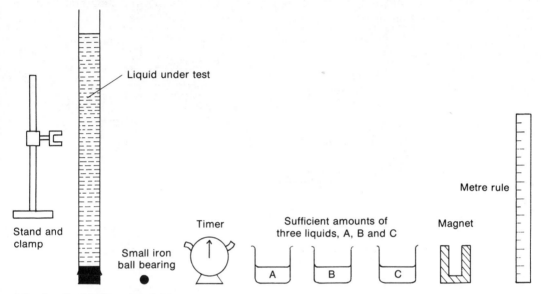

Describe how you would all use the equipment to measure the viscosity (resistance to flow) of the three liquids. Give an outline of the method you would use and the measurements you would take. How would you place the liquids in order of increasing viscosity using your results?

5 Two plastic syringes are joined by a length of hollow rubber tubing. One is empty, the other contains a liquid which also fills the connecting tube. A house brick rests against the plunger of the empty syringe as shown.

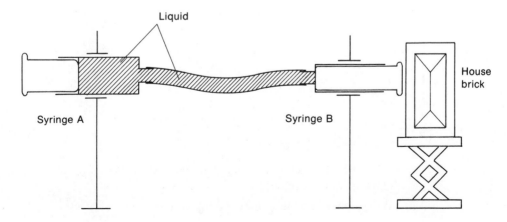

a) i)   What will happen when the plunger of syringe A is pushed in?

ii) Why does this happen?

b) The syringes and tubing are emptied and dried, and the experiment is repeated with air in syringe A. What will happen?

c) Use the diagram below to explain why a gas bubble in a car's brake fluid is dangerous.

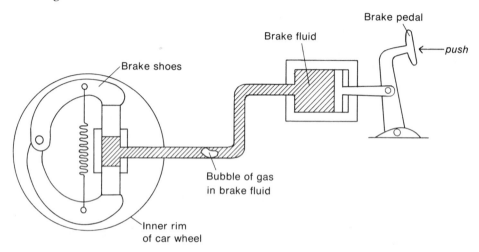

6 The diagram shows an alcohol thermometer, which uses an ethanol–dye mixture to indicate the temperature. Data on ethanol (and mercury, another liquid commonly used in thermometers) is given in the table.

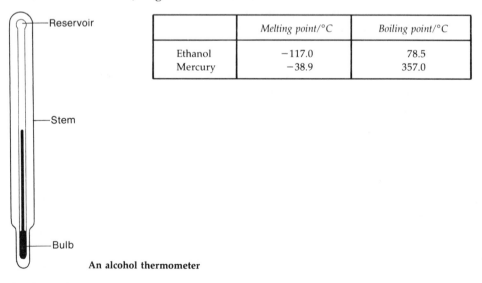

	Melting point/°C	Boiling point/°C
Ethanol	−117.0	78.5
Mercury	−38.9	357.0

An alcohol thermometer

a) i)   Why does the bulb of the thermometer have thick glass at the base but thin glass around the sides?

ii) Why is there a reservoir at the top of the stem?

b)   Copy and complete the following table by listing one advantage and one disadvantage of each liquid for use in a thermometer.

	Advantage	Disadvantage
Ethanol Mercury		

c)   The liquid in the alcohol thermometer freezes at $-118.5\,°C$. Comment on this in view of the melting point of ethanol given.

7   The boiling point of a liquid increases as the external pressure increases. Use this information to explain the following observations.

a)   If a cup of water is placed in an air-tight container and the air is removed using a vacuum pump, the water will boil without being heated.

b)   Food cooks more quickly in a pressure cooker.

c)   The accurately measured boiling point of a sample of pure water may change from one day to the next if there is an accompanying change in the weather.

d)   It is dangerous to remove the radiator cap when a car's water cooling system is overheating.

8   Two gas cylinders have been found. One is known to contain a poisonous gas under pressure, the other a partial vacuum, but they are identical in all other respects. In principle, would it be possible to identify the poison gas cylinder by weighing them?

Explain your answer.

9   Three rigid, hollow metal containers have tubes connected to beakers of water as shown in the diagram. All three contain air and are identical except for their internal conditions.

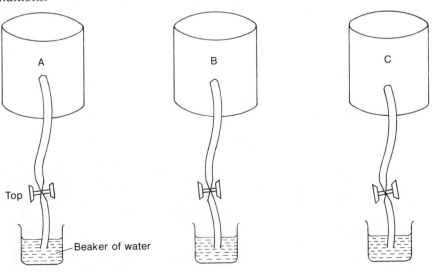

When the taps are opened, the following results are noted:

Container	Observations
A B C	The water level in the beaker drops Nothing happens Bubbles appear at the end of the tube

What can you deduce from these observations about the conditions inside each container before the taps were opened?

10 a) A partly inflated balloon is placed inside a glass container, which is then evacuated. As the air is pumped out of the container what will happen to

  i)   the number of molecules in the balloon?

  ii) the volume of the balloon?

  b) Explain why weather balloons, designed to fly at high altitude, are only partly inflated at launch.

11

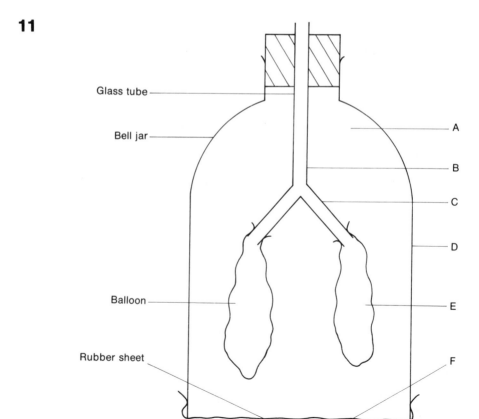

Glass tube

Bell jar

A

B

C

D

Balloon

E

Rubber sheet

F

The diagram on the previous page represents a model of the human thorax.

a) What parts of the human thorax do the labels A to F represent?

b) Describe and explain what happens when

    i)   the rubber sheet is pulled down

    ii) the rubber sheet is pushed up

c) What part of breathing does each of these actions represent?

d) In what way is this an inaccurate demonstration of how we breathe in and out?

12 a) Copy and complete the following table to show a test used to identify each of the following gases.

Gas	Details of the test	Expected result in a positive test
Hydrogen Oxygen Chlorine Carbon dioxide Hydrogen chloride Ammonia		

b) An acidic gas X dissolved in water readily. The solution was then electrolysed and two gases, Y and Z, were produced.

Y burned with a squeaky pop.
Z bleached moist litmus paper.

Suggest names for the gases X, Y and Z.

13 The table below gives information on the properties of six gases.

Name	Density compared to air	Solubility in water
Hydrogen	Less	Low
Oxygen	Approximately equal	Low
Chlorine	Greater	Moderate
Carbon dioxide	Greater	Moderate
Hydrogen chloride	Greater	High
Ammonia	Less	High

Copy and complete the table below, to show which gas (or gases) could be collected using the types of apparatus shown.

Method	Gases collected using this method
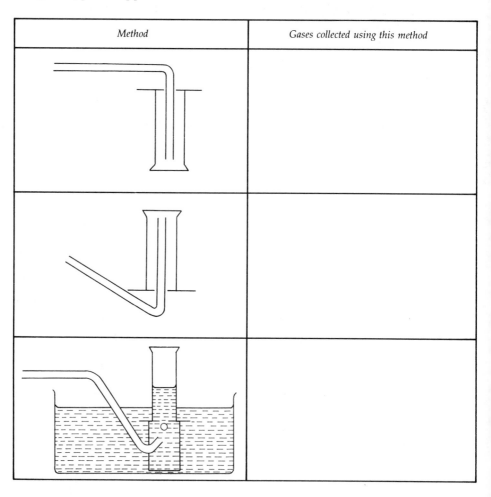	

14   Several common laboratory gases can be produced using the apparatus shown, with a suitable choice of solution and solid.

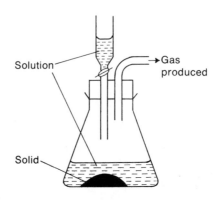

a) Copy the diagram.

b) Copy and complete the table below by giving the names of a suitable solution and solid for producing each gas.

Gas	Solution	Solid
Hydrogen		
Oxygen		
Chlorine		
Carbon dioxide		
Hydrogen chloride		

c) Name one substance which could be used to dry all of the gases mentioned in part a).

15 The apparatus shown below is used to find the change in volume of a fixed mass of gas when the pressure is increased. The experiment is carried out at constant temperature.

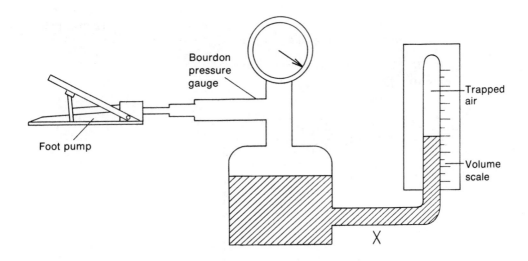

a) i) Write down a short description of what you would do, and what readings you would take, when carrying out this experiment.

ii) What precaution would you include to allow the air to remain at its original temperature?

b) The graph overleaf was produced using results from such an experiment. Use the graph to predict what will happen to the volume of a sample of gas when the pressure is doubled at constant temperature.

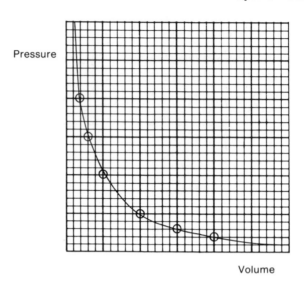

Pressure

Volume

c) If a bubble of air was trapped in the apparatus at point X, what effect (if any) would this have on the results of the experiment?

16 a) A sample of gas at 1 atmosphere pressure is contained in a 100 cm³ cylinder. If the piston is moved half way down the cylinder and no change in temperature occurs, what is the new value of

    i)   the volume occupied by the gas

    ii) the pressure exerted by the gas?

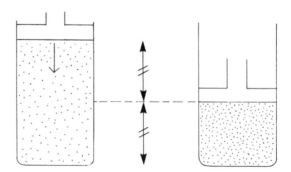

b) In another experiment, the piston is moved down slowly so that the volume occupied by the gas is halved while the temperature remains constant. As a result of this, what has happened to

    i)   the number of molecules in the cylinder?

    ii) the density of the gas?

    iii) the number of collisions per second by molecules on the piston?

17 The apparatus below is used to measure the pressure of a gas, at constant volume, as the temperature increases.

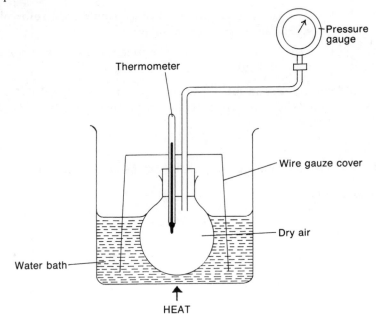

a) Why is a round-bottom flask preferred, and why is a cover needed?

b) What would happen to

   i)   the mass of gas in the flask?
   ii) the pressure of the gas

   as the temperature increases?

c) If the experiment is carried out at an external pressure of 1 atmosphere, what is the maximum temperature reached by the gas in the experiment?

d) Sketch the graph of pressure against temperature which you would obtain from such an experiment.

e) Explain in terms of the kinetic theory why the pressure of a gas changes as the temperature increases.

18 The volume of a sample of dry nitrogen was measured as its temperature changed. The pressure was maintained at 1 atmosphere throughout the experiment. The results obtained are shown in the table below:

Temperature/°C	20	50	100	150	200	250
Volume/cm³	48.1	53.0	61.2	69.4	77.6	85.8

a) Plot a graph of volume (y-axis) against temperature (x-axis). The x-axis scale should begin at −300 °C and extend to +300 °C with 50 °C per division. Draw the best-fit straight line through the points, and label it 'line A'.

b) Use your graph to estimate the volume of the nitrogen at −100 °C and 1 atmosphere.

c) i) At what temperature would the sample have zero volume? What is the significance of this temperature?

   ii) What would happen to the nitrogen gas on cooling before this temperature was reached?

d) Draw a second line on your graph, labelled 'line B', which shows what you would expect to happen if the experiment was repeated at a constant pressure of 2 atmospheres.

19 The diagram below shows what happens inside a petrol engine cylinder.

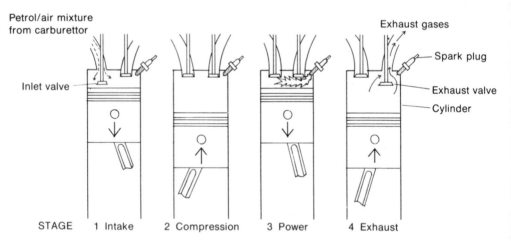

Petrol vapour and air are drawn in to the cylinder. The mixture is squeezed together and then exploded by a spark. The explosion pushes down the piston and this gives the engine power.

During which stage or stages does

a) a chemical change occur?

b) the pressure and temperature in the cylinder increase?

c) the pressure and temperature in the cylinder increase without any chemical change?

d) the mean density of the gases in the cylinder increase?

e) the number of molecules in the cylinder increase?

20 a) Copy and complete this sentence, choosing the correct word given in the brackets:

   Diffusion results in particles moving from a region of (high/low) concentration to a region where they are (less/more) concentrated.

b) i) Stephen drops a stinkbomb in the corner of the classroom. Explain why it will very soon be smelt at the other side of the room.

ii) Why will the smell eventually disappear?

c) Meena carefully placed a single crystal of potassium permanganate (a soluble, purple compound) at the bottom of a beaker of water. The beaker was then left undisturbed for several days. What would she see on returning to the experiment? Explain what happened.

21 Copy and complete the following sentences about diffusion in living organisms by filling in the missing words:

a) **Diffusion** is important because it is the main way in which living organisms obtain the things they _____, and get rid of their _____ products. Here are some examples.

b) Oxygen continually _____ into the body of *Amoeba* and _____ continually diffuses out. This is because *Amoeba* constantly uses _____ and produces _____.

c) The same process also occurs in our lungs. The _____ diffuses from the lungs into the blood. The _____ diffuses from the blood into the lungs.

d) In our gut soluble food substances such as glucose, _____ from the intestine into the surrounding blood capillaries.

e) Green leaves obtain the gas _____ for photosynthesis by diffusion. It enters the leaf through small holes or pores.

f) Fishes obtain _____ from the water by diffusion. As the water flows past the gills, oxygen _____ from the water into the blood. Carbon dioxide diffuses from the _____ into the water.

22 a) Use the data on the ten substances below to produce a table, which shows the state of each substance at room temperature (25 °C).

Substance	Melting point/°C	Boiling point/°C
Selenium	217	685
Anisole	−38	154
Beryllium	1280	2477
Bromine	−7	59
Propane	−188	−42
Benzamide	132	290
Cobalt	1492	2900
Radon	−71	−62
Anthracene	216	340
Propyne	−103	−23

Solids	Liquids	Gases

b) List the substances in order of increasing boiling point.

c) Which substance is a liquid over the smallest range of temperature?

d) Which of the substances is gaseous at −50 °C?

e) Which substance has the lowest freezing point?

f) Which substance is a liquid at 2500 °C?

23 A substance melts at 92 °C and boils at 190 °C. The arrangement of particles in the substance at 50 °C and 250 °C are shown below.

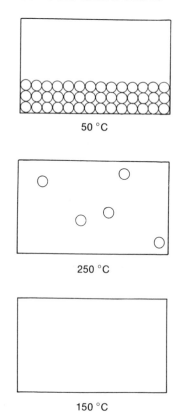

50 °C

250 °C

150 °C

a) Copy the diagram, with labels, and draw in the arrangement of particles you would expect at 150 °C.

b) At which of the three temperatures is the motion of the particles limited to vibration?

c) When the temperature of 10 g of the substance changes from 50 °C to 60 °C, state whether each of the following quantities increases, decreases, or stays the same:

i)   the number of particles present

ii) the average energy of the particles

iii) the density of the substance

3.1.2 Elements, Compounds and Mixtures

1   From the symbols shown, choose the correct symbol for each of the following elements.

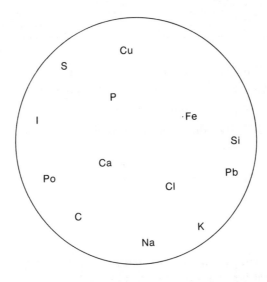

a)   iron   b)   sodium   c)   chlorine   d)   copper

e)   potassium   f)   carbon   g)   lead   h)   silicon

2   Copy and complete the following table, which compares the properties of metals and non-metals.

Metallic elements	Non-metallic elements
Conduct electricity	
Good conductors of heat	
	Brittle
Lustrous (shiny)	
Usually form positive ions	
	Oxides are generally acidic in solution

3 a) The following table lists the properties of five elements. The letters used are not the symbols for the elements.

Element	Solubility in water	Melting point (°C)	Electrical conductivity (solid)	Thermal conductivity
A	Reacts	39	Good	Good
B	Soluble	−101	Does not conduct	Poor
C	Insoluble	113	Does not conduct	Poor
D	Insoluble	−39	Good	Good
E	Insoluble	−157	Does not conduct	Poor

   i)   Which of the elements are metals?

   ii) Which of the non-metals are gaseous at room temperature (25 °C)?

   iii) Which of the elements is mercury?

   iv) Give two differences between metals and non-metals other than those mentioned in the table.

   b) i) Which non-metallic element conducts electricity?

       ii) Name one semi-metal (metalloid).

4 The following is part of the reactivity series for metals. (Hydroden is included, although it is a gaseous non-metal.)

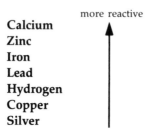

more reactive

Calcium
Zinc
Iron
Lead
Hydrogen
Copper
Silver

   a) Use the list to predict the outcome of the following reactions. For those instances when you think reaction will occur, write a word equation to show what happens.

       i)   Iron (III) oxide is heated with lead granules.

       ii) Lead foil is added to silver nitrate solution.

       iii) Zinc powder is heated with calcium oxide.

       iv) Copper is added to dilute hydrochloric acid.

       v)   Zinc is added to dilute hydrochloric acid.

   b) Explain why the elements at the bottom of the series were discovered before the elements at the top.

5 The metals in the list below are in order of increasing reactivity:

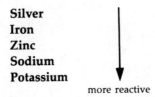

Silver
Iron
Zinc
Sodium
Potassium

more reactive

a) Which metal in the list is found native (uncombined)?

b) Why is sodium not found native?

c) Zinc can be obtained from zinc oxide by heating it with carbon. Name one other metal from the list which is extracted in this way.

d) What type of process is used to extract reactive metals such as sodium?

e) Write separate word equations for the reaction of sodium with oxygen, water and chlorine.

f) What would happen if a zinc rod was placed in silver nitrate solution?

g) Magnesium will react with zinc oxide but not potassium oxide. Sodium is more reactive than magnesium. Rewrite the list with magnesium in the correct place.

6 A student carried out the following experiment to investigate the effect of heat on a mixture of iron and sulphur. After heating for a few minutes, the mixture began to glow brightly. The glow spread through the contents of the tube after heating was stopped. When the tube had cooled the contents were tipped out onto a heat resistant bench mat. A grey solid had been formed.

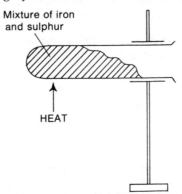

Mixture of iron
and sulphur

HEAT

a) Suggest two methods for separating the iron and sulphur in the original mixture.

b) Write down two pieces of information from the description of the experiment which suggest that a chemical reaction has taken place.

c) Name the compound formed in the reaction.

d) Which of the following methods could be used to separate the iron and sulphur in the compound?

   magnetism   **distillation**   **electrolysis**   **reaction with dilute acid**

7 The diagram below shows an unmanned rocket moving through space. The rocket uses liquid hydrogen and oxygen as its propellant.

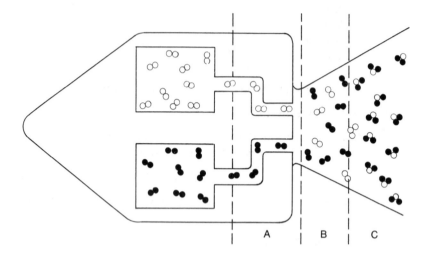

a) In which of the regions, A, B or C, is there

   i)   a compound?

   ii) two elements in a pure state?

   iii) a mixture of two elements?

b) Name the compound produced when hydrogen and oxygen react together.

c) Which of the following methods could be used to obtain hydrogen and oxygen from the compound produced when these elements react together?

   fractional distillation   chromatography   electrolysis
   crystallisation

8 Copy and complete the following table, which lists the differences between mixtures and compounds.

Mixtures	Compounds
No energy exchange with surroundings on formation.	
	Constituent elements can be recovered only by further reaction or electrolysis.
Mixtures can have any composition.	
	The properties of a compound rarely resemble those of its constituents.

9 Copy and complete the following sentences to show how you would separate the two substances in each mixture:

a) Sand and water can be separated by . . .

b) Iron filings and copper filings can be separated by . . .

c) Oil and water can be separated by . . .

d) Sand and sodium chloride (common salt) can be separated by . . .

e) Water and ethanol (alcohol) can be separated by . . .

f) A mixture of blue and red inks can be separated by . . .

10 a) Copy the diagram of the apparatus used to carry out fractional distillation of crude oil in the laboratory. Add labels at the positions indicated.

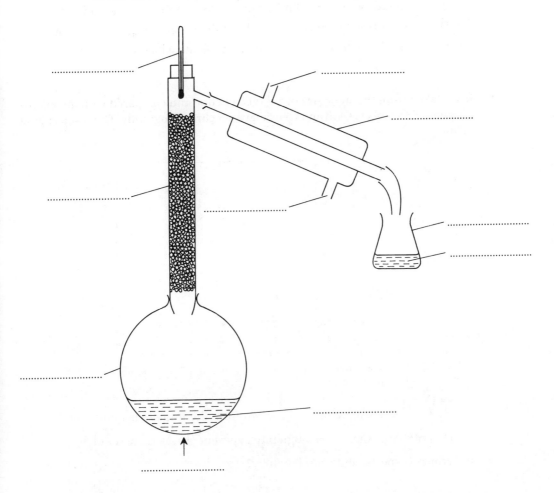

b) The following table gives details of some fractions collected during a distillation.

Fraction	Boiling point range/°C	Colour
1	160–190	Yellow
2	200–230	Orange
3	240–270	Brown

i) Is each fraction a pure compound? Explain your answer.

ii) Which fraction would be least viscous (most runny)?

iii) Which fraction would be most difficult to ignite, and would burn with the smokiest flame?

c) How does the apparatus separate crude oil into fractions? Give as much detail in your answer as you can.

d) Which of the following could be separated using fractional distillation?

A.   Liquids which mix and which have different melting points

B.   Liquids which mix and which have different boiling points

C.   Liquids with very similar boiling points which do not mix

D.   Liquids which mix, regardless of their melting or boiling points

E.   Liquids with very similar melting points which do not mix

11   Ink is taken from the signature of a forged cheque and compared with the ink from the pens of 3 suspects (A, B and C) using paper chromatography. The result is shown below:

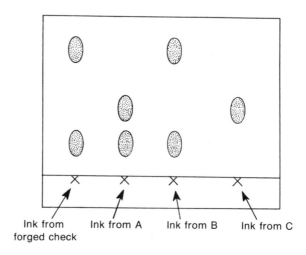

a) How could a sample of ink be taken from the forged cheque?

b) Describe how the chromatography experiment was carried out.

c) Which suspects could not be guilty?

3.1.3 The Periodic Table

1   Copy and complete the table below, which compares the characteristics of the alkali
metals and transition metals.

Transition metals	Alkali metals
Soft, low density metals	
	React slowly with water or not at all
Form colourless compounds	
	Form more than one compound with chlorine and other elements (variable valency)
	Metals and their compounds often useful as redox catalysts

2   Carbon, silicon and germanium are three of the elements in group 4 of the Periodic
Table. Group 4 is listed below.

C
Si
Ge
Sn
Pb

Some information on carbon and its compounds is given below:

Element	Density (g/cm³)	Formula of chloride	Formula of oxide
Carbon	2.3	CCl_4	CO_2

a)   Which elements are represented by the symbols Sn and Pb?

b)   Name one element in group 4 which is

   i)   a metal   ii)   a semi-metal (metalloid)   iii) a non-metal

c)   Predict the formulae of the following compounds:

   i)   silicon chloride   ii)   germanium oxide

d)   The density of germanium is 5.4 g/cm³. Estimate the density of silicon, showing
how you arrived at your answer.

e)   Describe one use of any *two* elements in group 4.

3 The boiling points of the first four elements in group 7 of the Periodic Table (the halogens) are given in the table below. The value for bromine has been left out.

Element	Boiling point/°C
Fluorine	−188
Chlorine	−101
Bromine	
Iodine	+184

a) Write down the chemical symbol of each element in the order shown.

b) Name one halogen which is a gas at room temperature (25 °C)

c) i) Write down an estimate for the boiling point of bromine. Explain how you arrived at your answer.

ii) Bromine is toxic. Draw a diagram of the apparatus you would use to test your prediction for the boiling point of bromine. Where would you carry out the experiment, and what precautions would you take?

4 Copy and complete the following sentences by choosing the correct word from the brackets.

a) The alkali metals are (soft/hard) and react (slowly/violently) with water.

b) Transition metals form many (coloured/colourless) compounds and have (high/low) densities.

c) Chlorine, a member of the (inert gases/halogens), forms a simple (positive/negative) ion.

d) Helium has (one/two) atoms in its molecules and reacts with (no/many) other elements.

e) Carbon is a (metallic/non-metallic) element which (conducts/does not conduct) electricity.

5

A portion of the Periodic Table is divided into 4 parts as shown. In which part (A–D) would you find:

a)   a metal which reacts violently with cold water?

b)   an element which doesn't form any compounds?

c)   a metal which has many coloured compounds?

d)   the element chlorine?

e)   a non-metal which conducts electricity?

f)   a gas which reacts with oxygen to form water?

g)   the metal with the highest melting point?

h)   an element X which forms an oxide X_2O_3?

6   In the Periodic Table shown below, the letters used are not the symbols of the elements. Choose the letter corresponding to an element which:

a)   forms a hydroxide which is strongly alkaline.

b)   forms a gaseous, acidic oxide in which atoms of the element and oxygen are in the ratio 1:2.

c)   has atomic number 14.

d)   has electron arrangement 2, 8, 7.

e)   readily forms an ion carrying the charge −2.

f)   forms more than one chloride.

g)   has similar chemical properties to L.

h)   is a non-metal which conducts electricity.

i)   has the largest relative atomic mass.

j)   readily forms an ion which has the same electron arrangement as X.

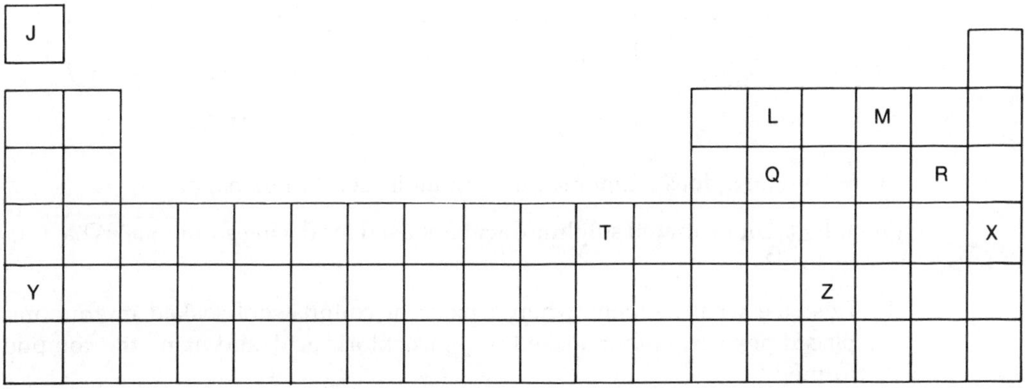

7   Some of the following statements concerning the Periodic Table are true, others are false. Copy them out, correcting any that are false.

    a)   In the Periodic Table, each row is called a period.

    b)   Elements in the same group have similar chemical properties.

    c)   There are more non-metals than metals in the Periodic Table.

    d)   In moving from left to right across the Periodic Table, elements become more metallic.

    e)   Elements in group 2 are called the halogens.

    f)   The alkali metals become more reactive as the group is descended.

    g)   The Periodic Table arranges the elements in order of increasing boiling point.

3.1.4 Acids, Alkalis and Salts

1   a)   Ammonia is very soluble in water. Explain why method 1 (below) is unsuitable for producing ammonia solution, while method 2 works well.

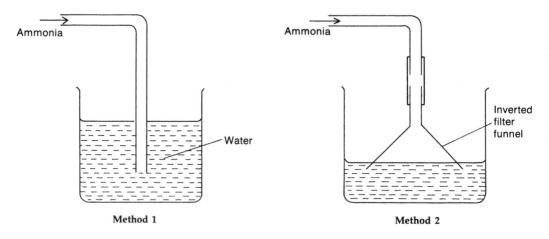

Method 1   Method 2

    b)   What effect does ammonia have on moist red litmus paper?

    c)   Why is concentrated sulphuric acid not used for drying ammonia? What is used instead?

    d)   Describe what happens when a piece of cotton wool soaked in ammonia is placed next to another soaked in hydrochloric acid, and name the compound formed.

2 The apparatus below is used to synthesise ammonia in the laboratory.

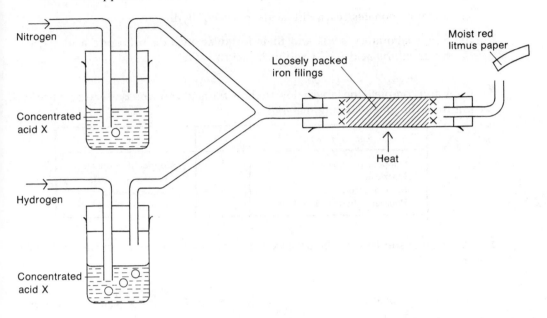

a) The gases are taken from cylinders, and must be supplied to the reaction vessel in the ratio 1 part nitrogen to 3 parts hydrogen. Using the apparatus as shown, describe one simple method of checking whether the ratio is approximately correct.

b) i) What is 'concentrated acid X' and what is its purpose?

   ii) What is the purpose of the iron filings?

c) If the experiment was successful, what would happen to the moist red litmus paper?

d) Describe another test for ammonia, involving concentrated hydrochloric acid, which could be used instead of the moist red litmus paper.

e) Why must this experiment be performed in a fume cupboard?

f) Name two *compounds* which produce ammonia when heated together.

3 The following statements refer to acids. Some are correct, others are incorrect. Copy them out, correcting those that are wrong.

a) Acidic solutions have a pH less than 7.

b) All substances which contain hydrogen are acids.

c) Weak acids that are safe to taste, taste sour.

d) Acidic solutions turn red litmus paper blue.

e) All acids contain the element hydrogen.

f) Acids are neutralised by alkalis.

g) Metal carbonates react with acids, releasing hydrogen.

h) Some laboratory acids and their formulae include sulphuric acid (H_2SO_4), hydrochloric acid (HCl) and nitric acid (NaOH).

4 Copy and complete the table below to show the acid you would use to produce each salt from the given starting material.

Starting material	Acid	Salt produced
Copper (II) oxide Magnesium Sodium carbonate Potassium hydroxide solution		Copper (II) sulphate Magnesium nitrate Sodium chloride Potassium phosphate

5 Magnesium sulphate can be prepared using the following steps, but *not* in the order shown.

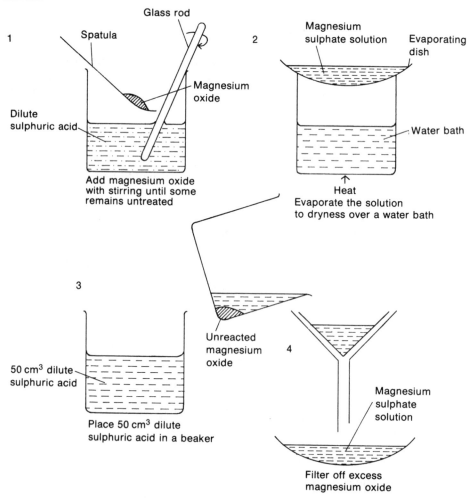

a) Draw the diagrams in the correct sequence.

b) Why is the magnesium oxide added until some remains unreacted?

c) Why is the solution heated to dryness using a water bath?

d) Using this method, powdered magnesium sulphate is obtained. How would you modify the method to obtain large crystals of magnesium sulphate?

e) An alternative method for producing magnesium sulphate involves adding magnesium ribbon to dilute sulphuric acid. Explain why this method, using the reaction between a metal and an acid, would *not* be suitable for making

    i)   copper (II) sulphate

    ii) sodium sulphate

f) What is the pH of magnesium sulphate solution?

6 The effect of three salts on water is shown in the table. Give brief details of the method you would use to prepare a sample of each salt from the starting material indicated. Explain why each method is suitable for that particular salt.

Salt	Effect of adding the salt to water	Starting material
Potassium sulphate	Dissolves	Potassium carbonate
Barium sulphate	Insoluble	Barium chloride solution
Aluminium chloride	Reacts	Aluminium

7 Look at the following pH ranges:

    pH 1–3
    pH 4–6
    pH 7
    pH 8–10
    pH 11–13

Which pH range would apply to each of the following solutions?

a) concentrated sodium hydroxide solution

b) an antacid medicine

c) water

d) concentrated hydrochloric acid

e) dilute ammonia solution

8   The table below shows the pH at which some indicators undergo a colour change.

Indicator name	pH of solution at colour change	'Acid' colour	'Alkali' colour
Thymol blue	2	Red	Yellow
Bromophenol blue	4	Yellow	Blue
Methyl red	5	Red	Yellow
Phenol red	8	Yellow	Red
Phenolphthalein	9	Colourless	Red
Thymolphthalein	10	Colourless	Blue

a)   Which indicator(s) would be red in a solution of pH 6?

b)   Which indicator(s) could be used to distinguish between two samples, one of dilute ammonia solution (pH 9), the other of dilute sodium hydroxide solution (pH 12)?

c)   What colour would bromophenol blue be in

i)   a solution of pH 14?

ii)   a solution of pH 4?

3.1.5 Petrochemicals

1   Crude oil is an example of a fossil fuel. At an oil refinery, it is cleaned then separated into fractions by fractional distillation. Part of the fractionating column is drawn below.

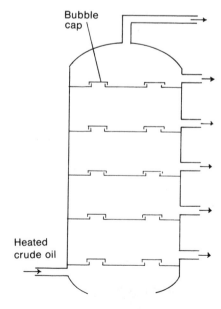

a) What is a fossil fuel? Name two other fossil fuels.

b) Explain how a fractionating column separates crude oil into fractions, referring to the diagram in your answer.

c) Arrange the following fractions in order of increasing boiling point.

    LPG   **kerosine**   **naphtha**   **heavy oil**

d) Write down a major use for any *two* of the above fractions.

e) Explain what is meant by the description of fossil fuels as **non-renewable** energy sources.

2 The table shows some information about some hydrocarbons known as alkanes.

Name	Molecular formula	Relative molecular mass	Boiling point (°C)	Heat of combustion (kJ/mol)
Methane	CH_4	16	−161	−890
Ethane		30	−89	−1560
Propane	C_3H_8	44	−42	−2220
Butane	C_4H_{10}	58		−2877
Pentane	C_5H_{12}	72	+36	−3509
Hexane	C_6H_{14}	86	+69	

a) Use the pattern in the formulae to predict the formula of ethane.

b) i) How do the boiling points change as the relative molecular mass of the hydrocarbons increases?

   ii) Use a graphical method to estimate the boiling point of butane.

c) Calculate the difference between successive values of the heats of combustion, and use your result to estimate the heat of combustion of hexane in kJ/mol.

d) Which of the following hydrocarbons belong to the alkane family?

    $C_{10}H_{22}$ C_6H_6 $C_{12}H_{26}$ C_2H_4 $C_{25}H_{52}$

3 The experiment below demonstrates the combustion of petrol in a car engine.

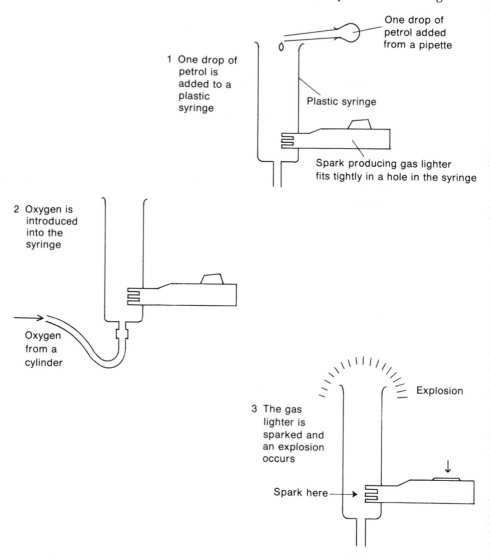

1 One drop of
  petrol is
  added to a
  plastic
  syringe

One drop of
petrol added
from a pipette

Plastic syringe

Spark producing gas lighter
fits tightly in a hole in the syringe

2 Oxygen is
  introduced
  into the
  syringe

Oxygen
from a
cylinder

Explosion

3 The gas
  lighter is
  sparked and
  an explosion
  occurs

Spark here

a) From what naturally occurring material is petrol obtained?

b) Why should the syringes used in this experiment be made from plastic and not glass?

c) Which part of the car engine is represented by the gas lighter?

d) Acidic nitrogen oxides produced in car engines are pollutants. How are they formed?

e) Name the carbon compound produced when petrol burns in

  i)   a rich supply of oxygen

  ii) a poor supply of oxygen

4 Polyethene and polyphenylethene (polystyrene) are in widespread use as plastics. The structural formulae of the polymers are shown below.

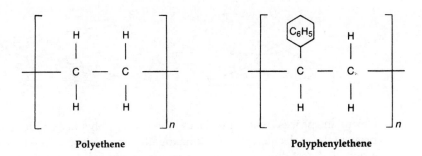

Polyethene   Polyphenylethene

a) What does n mean in these formulae?

b) Both polymers are made from alkenes such as ethene. Which bond in alkenes enables them to polymerise?

ethene, C_2H_4

c) Polyethene is more elastic than polyphenylethene (polystyrene). How does the different shape of the long-chain molecules in each polymer explain this difference?

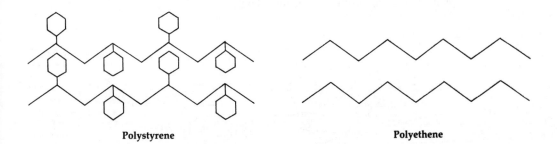

Polystyrene   Polyethene

d) i) Name the products formed when polyethene burns in a plentiful supply of air.

ii) What problems are associated with disposing of waste polyethene by burning it?

5   The arrangement of long-chain molecules in low density (A) and high density (B)
polyethene can be represented as shown in the diagrams below.

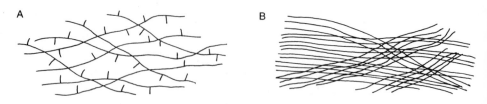

A   B

During the process which produces low density polyethene, side chains form which
prevent the molecules from packing together more closely. The high density form is
more rigid and does not soften at temperatures below 100 °C.

a)   Using labelled copies of the diagrams, explain the difference in density between
the two types of polythene.

b)   Which form would you expect to have the greatest mechanical strength? Give
your reasons.

c)   Which type of polyethene would be more suitable for the following applications?

i)   a washing up bowl

ii)   a carrier bag

iii) a felt-tip pen

d)   Explain why a carrier bag made from polyethene is a greater potential hazard to
the environment than one made from paper.

6   The arrangement of molecules in a **thermosoftening** plastic differs from that in a
thermosetting plastic. Molecular chains in the thermoset are cross-linked, a feature
which affects the properties of the plastic.

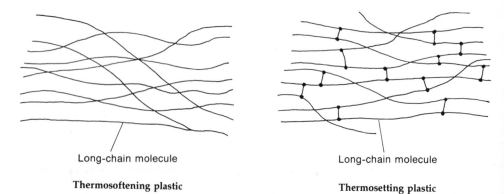

Long-chain molecule   Long-chain molecule

Thermosoftening plastic   **Thermosetting plastic**

a)   Name one thermosoftening and one thermosetting plastic.

b) Copy and complete the following table, which compares the properties of thermosoftening and thermosetting plastics.

Thermosoftening	Thermosetting
	Hard and brittle
Soften and melt on heating	
Soluble in organic solvents	

7   The following items are now made from a polymer (plastic) rather than the traditional material listed. Copy the table and add two advantages and one disadvantage of the new material over the old.

Item	Old material	New material	Advantages	Disadvantage
Drainpipe	Ferrous metal	Polyvinyl chloride (PVC)	Does not corrode, easily cut	Not as tough
Chair	Wood	Polypropylene		
Wire insulation	Rubber	PVC		
Carrier bag	Paper	Polyethene		
Packaging	Straw	Polystyrene		
Rope	Jute	Nylon		

3.1.6 More Chemicals in our Lives

1   From the list of household chemicals, choose
   a)   an antacid medicine
   b)   a painkiller
   c)   a bleach
   d)   a solution of a dilute acid
   e)   an alkaline gas in solution
   f)   a sedative
   g)   a gaseous fuel
   h)   a carbohydrate
   i)   a polymer
   j)   a neutral salt

> **sodium hydrogen carbonate**   **aspirin**   **sodium chlorate (I)**
> **vinegar**   **ammonia**   **ethanol**   **methane**   **glucose**
> **polystyrene**   **sodium chloride**

2 The information on two common fertilisers is given in the table below:

Name	Formula	Solubility in water
Ammonium nitrate	NH_4NO_3	Dissolves readily
Urea	CON_2H_4	Dissolves slowly

a) How many atoms are there in one formula unit of ammonium nitrate?

b) Which element is responsible for the fertilising action of these compounds?

c) Explain why there is an ever-increasing demand for fertilisers.

d) Write down one method of fertilising soil which does not involve man-made chemicals.

e) What property of urea makes it a slow acting fertiliser?

f) Which acid must be reacted with ammonia to make ammonium nitrate?

g) Give one problem which might arise from the direct use of ammonia solution as a fertiliser.

h) The large-scale use of fertilisers has given rise to some environmental problems. Briefly describe two of these.

3 A mixture of ammonium nitrate and calcium carbonate, known as nitrochalk, is often used on acidic soil. Explain how this mixture fertilises soil and reduces the acidity.

4 Read the passage below, then answer the questions which follow.

Some phosphorus-containing insecticides are in use today to rid crops of pests. Many are also toxic to mammals, so great care must be taken in choosing a safe insecticide. Some have such a high toxicity that only 0.000 01 g per kg body mass is fatal to humans.

When applied to plants, these insecticides become part of the plant's system and are very effective in killing insects all over the plant. One such compound, called malathion, has proved to be useful in treating head lice infestation in humans. Malathion has a high toxicity to insects but low toxicity to mammals. Unfortunately, it smells of rotten cabbages! The structural formula of malathion is given below.

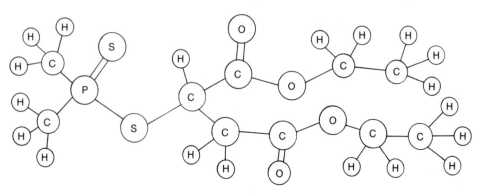

a) Why are phosphorus-based insecticides potentially dangerous?

b) Is the type of plant insecticide discussed in the passage best described as local or systemic? Explain your choice.

c) If an insecticide has a toxicity of 0.000 01 g/kg body mass, what is the minimum amount which would be fatal to a 70 kg man?

d) State one advantage and one disadvantage of the insecticide malathion for treating head lice infestation.

e) Substitute numerical values for v, w, x, y and z in the molecular formula for malathion:

$$C_v \ H_w \ P_x \ S_y \ O_z$$

5 a) Copy and complete the table below, which gives examples of some types of drug and their effect on the body.

Effect on the body	Type	Example
Analgesic		Kills pain
Antacid	Sodium hydrogencarbonate	
Anaesthetic		
	Penicillin	
	Caffeine	Keeps you awake and active
	Ethanol (alcohol)	
	LSD	Causes hallucinations

6 The molecules of two drugs, aspirin and caffeine, are shown below.

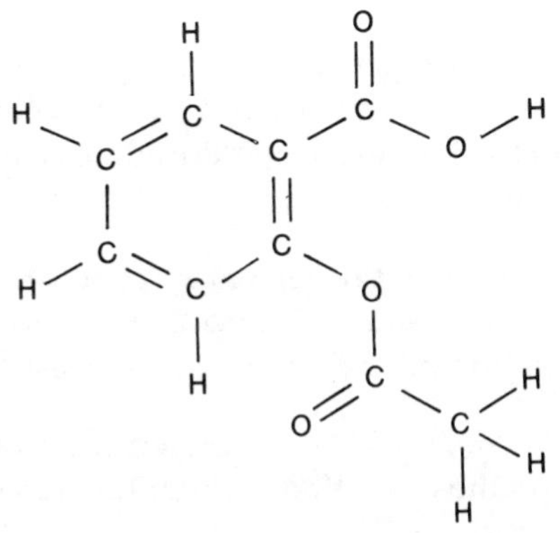

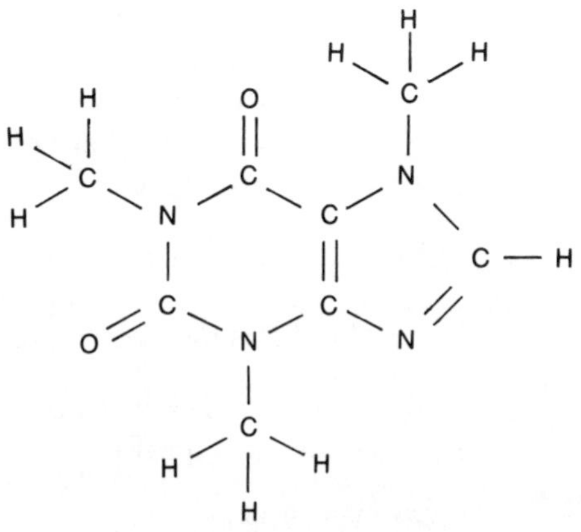

a) What is the difference between a drug and a medicine?

b) How many bonds do the atoms of

   i)   hydrogen
   ii) oxygen
   iii) nitrogen
   iv) carbon

   form with other atoms in these molecules?

c) Write down the molecular formulae of aspirin and caffeine.

d) What action do *each* of these drugs have on the body?

e) Name two drinks which contain caffeine.

7 For almost 100 years, the only anaesthetics in use were nitrous oxide (N_2O), ether ($C_4H_{10}O$) and chloroform ($CHCl_3$). None of these is very effective, and each has a number of disadvantages. Nitrous oxide does not put patients into a deep sleep, some operating theatres which used ether were destroyed in explosions or fires, and chloroform is believed to cause damage to the heart and liver.

Research during the last 50 years has produced a number of highly successful anaesthetics. Some compounds with anaesthetic properties are listed in the table below.

Molecular formula of the compound	Boiling point/°C	LD_{50}	Percentage halogen content by mass
$CHCl_3$	61	2.6	89
$CHFCl_2$	9	6.4	87
CF_3CHBr_2	73	2.0	90
$CF_3CHClBr$	50	3.6	87
$CHFClCF_2OCHF_2$	57	8.0	71

a) i)   What is a halogen?
   ii) Compounds containing carbon, hydrogen and halogens are more likely to cause explosions as the halogen content decreases. Place the compounds in the table in order of increasing risk of explosion during use, and indicate clearly which is the most dangerous.

b) The number listed under the heading LD_{50} is the percentage concentration of the compound in air needed to kill 50% of a sample of mice ('LD' stands for 'lethal dose'). Using these figures, place the compounds in order of increasing toxicity.

c) Compounds which boil between 40 °C and 70 °C are preferred as they are easy to use in vaporisers. Which compounds listed boil within this range?

d) Which compound is the most satisfactory anaesthetic? Explain your choice.

8   A home wine-making kit contains the following items:

> **1 demijohn (large bottle)**
> **1 airlock**
> **1 heating unit (controlled by a thermostat)**
> **sugar**
> **grape juice**
> **yeast**
> **yeast nutrient**
> **sterilising tablets**

The procedure outlined below was followed during the production of one batch of wine.

After sterilising the glassware, the sugar, yeast, yeast nutrient and grape juice were dissolved in water and added to the demijohn. The heater and airlock were fitted, and the demijohn placed in a dark cupboard for eight weeks. During this time, the bubbles of gas coming through the airlock were counted for one minute each day, and the results used to plot the graph.

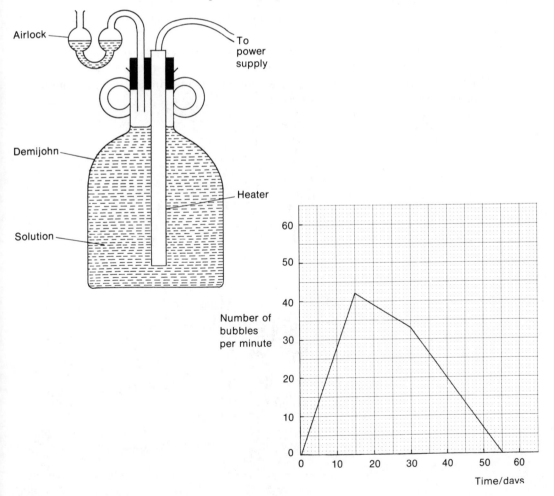

a) Why is it important to sterilise the equipment used in making wine?

b) i) Name the process in which sugar is converted into ethanol (alcohol) using yeast.

   ii) Which gas is a by-product of this process?

c) i) Explain why the airlock is necessary.

   ii) Why is it important to prevent the temperature from becoming too high or too low?

d) i) After how long did the rate of ethanol production reach a maximum?

   ii) When did ethanol production stop?

e) What method would you use to separate ethanol from the solution in the demijohn?

f) 4 moles of ethanol (C_2H_5OH) can be produced from 1 mole of sucrose ($C_{12}H_{22}O_{11}$).

   i) Calculate the maximum mass of ethanol that could, in theory, be obtained from 342 g sucrose.

   ii) Why is it unlikely that all the sugar will be converted into alcohol?

9 Ethanol, the alcohol present in beer, wine and spirits, can affect a person's ability to drive or operate machinery when present in the bloodstream at levels below the legal limit (80 mg in 100 cm^3 blood). The effects of drinking various amounts of alcohol are shown on the next page.

Drinks consumed	Approximate blood alcohol level (mg/100 cm³)	Effects
1 bottle of whisky	500	Death possible
¾ bottle of whisky	400	Unconsciousness, coma possible
6½ pints of beer	200	Loss of memory, double vision, difficulty in walking
5 pints of beer or 10 whiskies	150	Loss of self-control, slurred speech
-------------------------------	80 mg legal limit	-------------------------------
2 pints of beer or 4 whiskies	60	Judgement is markedly impaired
1 pint of beer or 2 glasses of wine	30	Likelihood of an accident begins to increase

The reaction of a person to alcoholic drink depends on several factors, including body mass. In an average individual, the amount of alcohol in the bloodstream will rise gradually for about 1 hour after drinking a pint of beer, then fall to zero after a further 2 hours. The graph below shows the blood alcohol level of a person, from midday to midnight, on a day when he or she consumes alcoholic drinks at lunch time and after leaving work.

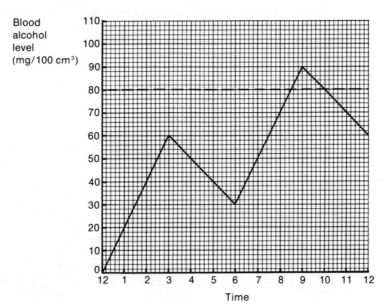

a) Which of the following terms describes the action of ethanol?

   stimulant   **depressant**   **narcotic**

b) How many i) single whiskies ii) glasses of wine are equivalent to 1 pint of beer?

c) i) Give two factors, apart from body mass, which will affect a person's response to alcoholic drink.

   ii) Use the information provided to estimate the minimum number of pints of beer needed to raise the amount of alcohol in the bloodstream above the legal limit.

d) Use the graph to answer the following questions:

   i) For how long is the person's blood alcohol level over the legal limit?

   ii) What is the rate of decrease of blood alcohol in mg/100 cm³ blood/hour?

   iii) Someone goes to bed at midnight with a blood alcohol level of 200 mg/100 cm³. Is it likely that his or her blood alcohol level will be below the legal limit when he or she is driving to work at 7.00 a.m.?

e) Which organ in the body breaks down alcohol in the bloodstream?

f) Describe two serious health problems caused by prolonged heavy drinking.

10 Read the following passage and answer the questions which follow.

   Before 1856, dyes were obtained from animals, plants and minerals. Woad, a blue dye extracted from a plant of the same name, was used by ancient tribes as a body dye, while the crimson dye cochineal was extracted from crushed insect shells. Lead compounds were used in paint, but this is much less common today. The variety of colours available increased following W.H. Perkins' discovery of **synthetic** 'coal tar' dyes in the nineteenth century.

   There are many types of dye in use today, including **mordant dyes** and **reactive dyes**. With mordant dyeing, a piece of cloth is placed in a bath containing a solution of aluminium ions (the mordant). It is then transferred to a second bath which contains hydroxide ions. A precipitate is formed on the fibres of the cloth. When the cloth is added to a solution containing the dye, the coloured material attaches itself to the precipitate. Colours obtained in this way are not particularly **fast**.

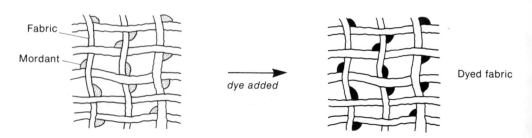

Fabric

Mordant

dye added

Dyed fabric

Reactive dyes become attached to the fabric directly. They consist of large molecules which can be drawn in the following simplified way:

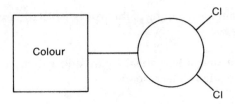

When cloth is dyed, the chlorine atoms in the dye are displaced during a chemical reaction with the cloth. Colours obtained in this way are bright and do not fade with washing.

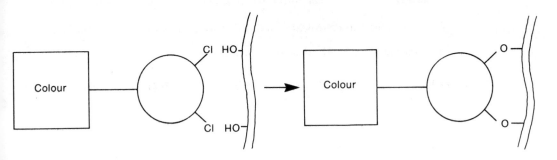

a) What is meant by the words 'fast' and 'synthetic' as used in the passage?

b) Suggest a chemical name for the mordant.

c) Explain why ammonia solution produces a precipitate with the mordant.

d) When a reactive dye bonds with a fibre as shown above, what other product is formed?

e) Explain why cloth coloured with a reactive dye is less likely to fade with washing than one coloured with a mordant dye.

f) Design a fair test to compare the resistance to fading in light of two identical pieces of red cloth – one coloured with a mordant dye the other with a reactive dye.

11 Read the following passage and then answer the questions.

Soap can be made by boiling a fat or oil with sodium hydroxide solution. The soap is separated from the reaction mixture by adding a concentrated solution of sodium chloride. This causes the soap to form a solid skin on the surface of the solution. Another product of the reaction is the alcohol glycerol which can be **isolated** using distillation. **Excess** sodium chloride solution is tapped off and **recycled**. After separation, the soap is washed, dried, scented (and coloured if required) before being pressed into tablets.

a) Use the information provided to draw a flow diagram for the production of soap.

b) Explain the meaning of the words 'isolated', 'excess' and 'recycled' as used in the passage.

c) Name one other metal hydroxide which could be used instead of sodium hydroxide to make soap.

d) In hard water, calcium ions react with soap to form an insoluble compound (scum):

$$2C_{17}H_{35}CO_2Na\,(aq) + Ca^{2+}\,(aq) \longrightarrow (C_{17}H_{35}CO_2)_2Ca\,(s) + 2\,Na^+\,(aq)$$

   soap   calcium ion   scum   sodium ions

   i) How does the chemical equation show that scum is insoluble?

   ii) Describe one method of removing calcium ions from hard water.

e) What precautions would you take when making soap on a small scale in the laboratory?

12 A soap or detergent molecule may be thought of as having an electrically charged 'head' which likes water and hates grease or oil, and a hydrocarbon 'tail' which likes grease or oil and hates water.

Tail   Head

Use this information to help you to explain each of the following observations.

a) Oil and water do not mix, but when a few drops of detergent are added and the mixture stirred, the oil disperses and a milky sol is formed. The oil remains dispersed if the sol is left to stand.

b) With care, a pin can be made to float on water. If detergent is carefully added, the pin sinks and cannot be refloated.

c) Water droplets do not soak in quickly with some types of cloth, but detergent solution is quickly absorbed.

d) Greasy clothes can be cleaned more efficiently by agitating in detergent solution; water alone has little effect.

13 Washing powders are complex mixtures. One type, Serpil, contains the following ingredients:

>   detergent and soap
>   enzymes
>   bleach
>   sodium phosphate
>   perfume

a) Which ingredient is added to

   i)   give the clothes a pleasant smell

   ii) improve the wetting power of water, and to remove grease stains

   iii) remove stains such as egg yolk and blood in a low temperature (30–40 °C) soak?

b) An advertisement for Serpil states that the powder 'digests dirt and stains'. Is this a fair claim? Explain your answer.

c) The bleach works at high temperatures only. What problems would be caused by using a more powerful bleach which works at all temperatures?

d) Sodium phosphate removes the hardness in water. Why is soft water better for washing purposes?

e) Washing powders can be a source of pollution. If some washing water contaminated a pond, what effect would the following ingredients have on the organisms listed, and why?

Ingredient	Organism
i) sodium phosphate	pond-weed
ii) detergent	pond-skater (an insect which walks on the surface of the water)

14 a) What causes hardness in water?

b) What is the difference between temporary and permanent hardness?

c) Describe and explain one method for removing each type of hardness.

d) List two problems which occur in household appliances due to hard water.

15 a) In a colloidal system, what is the equivalent of

   i)   the solvent in a solution

   ii) the solute in a solution?

b) Describe how you would use a light beam to decide whether a detergent powder forms a solution or a sol when added to water.

c) Why is it not possible to make a colloid from two gases?

16 An iron(III) hydroxide sol can be prepared by adding a small volume of concentrated iron(III) chloride solution to a large excess of boiling water in a beaker. The process also produces some hydrochloric acid.

$$FeCl_3 \quad\quad + 3\,H_2O \longrightarrow Fe(OH)_3 \quad + 3\,HCl$$

concentrated   boiling   iron(III)   hydrochloric
solution   water   hydroxide   acid
                                sol

The sol can be purified by dialysis. A simple dialyser can be made as shown in the diagram.

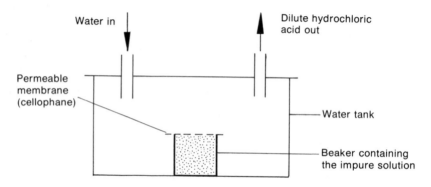

a) How could you show that the liquid leaving the dialyser was dilute hydrochloric acid and not pure water?

b) Explain why hydrochloric acid was present in the liquid leaving the dialyser, while the iron(III) hydroxide was not.

c) Give one important application of dialysis, and name the colloidal system involved.

17 Copy and complete the following table, which describes types of colloid.

Type of colloid	Dispersion medium	Disperse phase	Example(s)
Solid gel	Solid	Solid	
Solid emulsion	Solid		Butter
	Solid	Gas	Meringue
Paste	Liquid	Solid	
Emulsion	Liquid		Milk
Foam		Gas	
	Gas	Solid	Smoke
Aerosol			Cloud

18 The list below gives pairs of words used to describe materials. Choose one word from each pair to describe the materials listed.

> strong/weak   brittle/elastic   biodegradable/rot-proof
> transparent/opaque   electrical conductor/insulator

Materials:

a) rubber

b) glass

c) iron

d) bakelite (thermosetting plastic)

e) carbon (graphite)

f) polyvinyl chloride (PVC)

19 A student prepared a sample of lead borate glass using the following method.

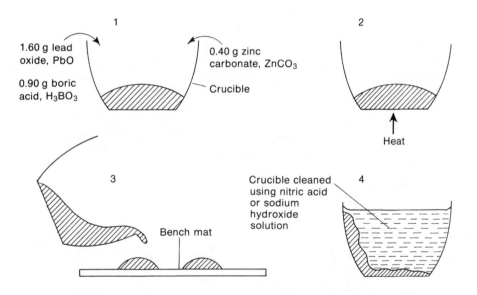

a) i)   Calculate the percentage by mass of lead oxide in the initial mixture.

ii) What precaution must be taken after working with the ingredients in this experiment?

b) What is the name of the gas produced when zinc carbonate is heated? Write a word equation for the decomposition.

c) Would lead borate glass be useful for making test tubes? Explain your answer.

d) One of the glass beads cracked and split into two pieces while cooling. Copy and complete the following explanation by choosing the correct word from the brackets:

    When a glass bead solidifies on the bench mat, the (inside/outside) cools more quickly, and begins to (expand/contract). This produces strains in the surface of the glass, which is weak under (compression/tension), and can lead to cracks which split the bead. To prevent this from happening, the glass should be cooled very (quickly/slowly) in a process called (quenching/annealing).

e) Traces of other metal oxides can be added to the melt to produce coloured glass. Which of the following oxides are likely to have this effect, and why?

    potassium oxide   **manganese oxide**   **copper oxide**
    magnesium oxide   **cobalt oxide**

f) The structures of boron oxide and lead borate glass are shown below and on the next page.

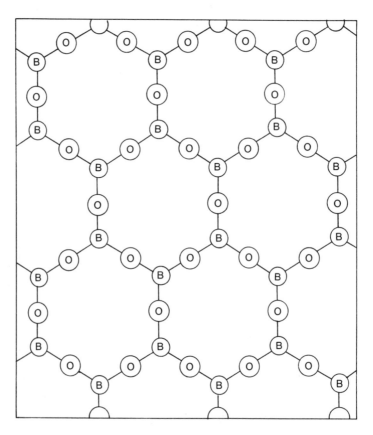

Crystalline boron oxide consists of chains of triangular units containing boron and oxygen atoms

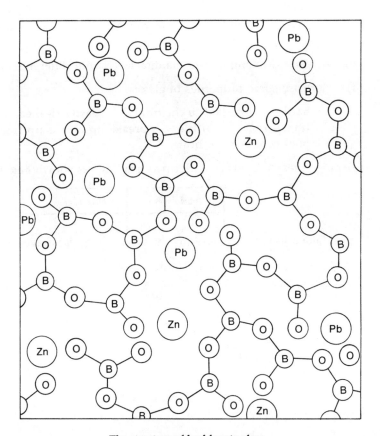

The structure of lead borate glass

i) Study the diagrams, then write down two similarities and two differences between the structures.

ii) Which substance, boron oxide or lead borate glass, has the higher melting point? Give reasons for your answer.

20 A sample of soda-lime glass is made by heating a mixture with the following composition.

sodium carbonate (Na_2CO_3)	15%
silicon dioxide (SiO_2)	75%
calcium carbonate ($CaCO_3$)	10%

a) List the elements present in soda-lime glass.

b) What mass of each ingredient must be taken to make 50 g of reaction mixture?

c) After heating, the mixture contains silicon dioxide together with oxides of sodium and calcium. What benefit is there in having metal oxides present in the melt?

d) List four household items made from glass. Is the type of glass the same for each object?

e) Why are drinking glasses manufactured with different compositions?

f) Here are some properties of glass:

> **hard**   **resistant to chemicals**   **easily cleaned**   **heat resistant**
> **transparent**   **brittle**   **breaks up into sharp fragments**
> **poor conductor of heat**

Arrange these properties under two headings as shown below:

Advantages	Disadvantages

g) Make a list of four ways in which recycling glass saves energy.

3.2 MAKING NEW MATERIALS

3.2.1 Classifying Change

1 Copy and complete the sentences below by choosing the correct word from the list.

> diffusion   burning   evaporation   dissolving   sublimation
> melting

a) Changing from solid to liquid is called _____.

b) An ink stain can be removed from clothing by _____ it in a solvent.

c) A puddle dries up after a shower because of _____.

d) When iodine is heated, a purple vapour is produced. This is an example of _____.

e) An open bottle of perfume can be smelt across a room because of _____.

f) _____ is a chemical change.

2 a) What is the difference between a **physical change** and a **chemical change**?

b) Draw up a table with two headings, *Physical changes and Chemical changes*. Place each of the following in your table under the correct heading.

> water boiling
> petrol burning
> sugar dissolving in water
> ice forming on a pond
> electricity flowing through copper wire

> a bicycle going rusty
> food being digested
> methane mixing with air
> chlorine bleaching litmus paper
> a resistor getting warm

3 a) Copy and complete the **fire triangle** by adding the missing ingredient:

b)   Which gas present in air is needed for combustion?

c)   Explain each of the following:

i)   A wet towel can be used to put out a fire in a chip pan.

ii)   Flammable liquids are often stored in an atmosphere of nitrogen.

iii) Water should not be used to put out electrical fires.

d)   Explain why blowing hard on the base of a camp fire makes the wood burn more vigorously, but blowing hard on a match puts the flame out.

4   In answering the following questions, choose one or more of the reaction types listed below:

hydrolysis   polymerisation   cracking   condensation

a)   Which reaction(s) result in large molecules being broken down into smaller ones?

b)   Which reaction(s) result in small molecules being converted into larger ones?

c)   Which reaction(s) take place when starch is converted into glucose during digestion?

d)   Which reaction types describe the production of nylon?

e)   Which type of reaction is the reverse of condensation?

f)   Which reaction(s) involve(s) the breaking of bonds using water?

5   Some types of chemical reaction are listed below.

decomposition   neutralisation   combustion
oxidation/reduction (redox)   dehydration

Which reaction type best describes the following changes?

a)   hexane + oxygen $\longrightarrow$ carbon dioxide + water

b)   calcium carbonate $\longrightarrow$ calcium oxide + carbon dioxide

c)   magnesium + copper oxide $\longrightarrow$ magnesium oxide + copper

d)   hydrochloric acid + sodium hydroxide $\longrightarrow$ sodium chloride + water

e)   sucrose $\longrightarrow$ carbon + water

6

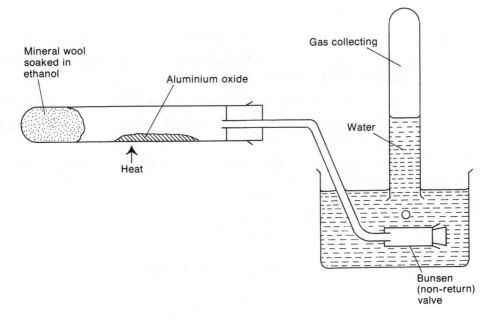

When heated and passed over hot aluminium oxide, ethanol is converted into ethene.

$$C_2H_5OH(g) \xrightarrow[Al_2O_3]{heat} C_2H_4(g) + H_2O(g)$$

a) What is the role of aluminium oxide in this experiment?

b) What *type* of reaction is this, in which water is removed from a compound?

c) Explain how a Bunsen (non-return) valve works and why it is necessary.

d) Ethene is an **unsaturated hydrocarbon**. What does this mean?

e) Give details of a simple chemical test which can be used to distinguish between saturated and unsaturated hydrocarbons.

7 The ore **malachite** contains copper carbonate. The sequence of steps below were carried out by a student to demonstrate how copper can be obtained from malachite.

    1. Heat powdered malachite in a hard glass test tube.
    2. After cooling, stir the contents of the tube into warm, dilute sulphuric acid until some solid remains unreacted.
    3. Filter the resulting solution.
    4. Add an iron nail to the filtrate, then pour off the solution after a few minutes.

a) Write down what you would *see* happening in step 1.

b) Write a word equation for the reaction occurring in step 1.

c) Explain why the solid was added until present *in excess* during step 2.

d) What type of reaction occurred in step 2?

e) Write a balanced chemical equation for the reaction in step 2.

f) Name the compound present in the filtrate after step 3.

g) What would happen to the appearance of the nail after step 4 showing that copper had been produced?

h) What type of reaction has occurred in step 4?

i) Name one metal which would *not* produce copper when added to the filtrate in step 4.

j) Name one other method which could be used to obtain copper from the filtrate obtained from step 3.

8

a) Using the information on the packet, calculate the number of grammes in one ounce.

b) The crisps in this packet are surrounded by nitrogen, which is at just over one atmosphere pressure. Any air inside the packet would reduce the shelf-life of the crisps because of a reaction with the fat in the crisps.

fat in crisps + air ⟶ aldehydes and organic acids
(nasty smells and unpleasant taste)

   i) Which gas present in air causes this reaction?

   ii) What type of reaction is this?

c) i) Name one gas (other than nitrogen) present in air which would not react with the fat in crisps. Why is nitrogen chosen for use in preference to the gas you have named?

   ii) Give two advantages of having the nitrogen in the packet at a higher pressure than the atmosphere.

d) Why are flammable liquids usually transported in an atmosphere of nitrogen?

9   The following experiment was set up to find the conditions needed for iron to rust.

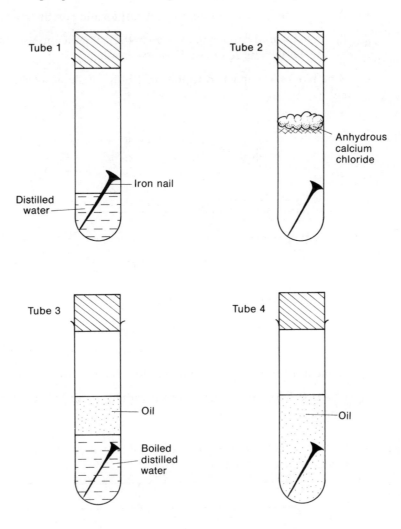

After setting up the tube as shown, they were left for two weeks.

a)   What was the purpose of the anhydrous calcium chloride in tube 2?

b)   Why was the water in tube 3

   i)   distilled

   ii)   boiled?

c)   What was the purpose of the oil layer in tube 3?

d)   The nail in tube 1 showed signs of rusting after two weeks, while the others did not. What conditions are needed for iron to rust?

e)   What was the purpose of tube 4?

f)   Explain how the rusting of iron can be classified as oxidation.

10 a) What is the chemical name for rust?

b) i) How does a layer of tin prevent rust forming on the inside of a can of fruit?

ii) What would happen to the iron in the can if the can was damaged and some of the tin was removed from the inside?

c) Zinc blocks are attached to the steel hulls of ships, as shown in the diagram below.

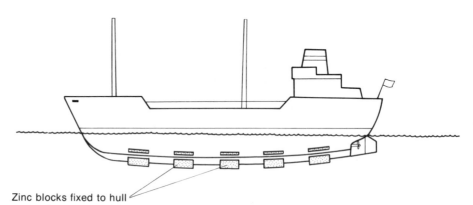

Zinc blocks fixed to hull

i) How does the zinc protect the ship from rusting?

ii) What would happen if copper blocks were used instead of zinc?

d) Name a metal which, when added to steel, produces a rust resistant alloy.

e) Describe one other method of preventing rusting. Explain how this method works.

11 a) Copy and complete the following table, which lists common definitions of oxidation and reduction.

Oxidation	Reduction
	Loss of oxygen
Loss of hydrogen	
	Gain of electrons

b) Use the table to decide whether the element in bold type in each of the following reactions has been oxidised or reduced.

i) The extraction of iron in a blast furnace

$$\mathbf{Fe_2O_3} + 3CO \longrightarrow 2Fe + 3CO_2$$

ii) The combustion of carbon monoxide above a coal fire

$$2\mathbf{CO} + O_2 \longrightarrow 2CO_2$$

iii) The production of aluminium at the cathode during electrolysis

$$\mathbf{Al^{3+}} + 3e^- \longrightarrow Al \quad (e^- = \text{an electron})$$

iv) The reaction of sodium with water

$$2Na + 2H_2O \longrightarrow 2NaOH + H_2$$

v) The reaction of lead with silver nitrate solution

$$Pb + 2AgNO_3 \longrightarrow Ag + Pb(NO_3)_2$$

c) Explain what is meant by a 'redox' reaction using one of the above reactions to illustrate your answer.

3.2.2 Chemicals of Life

---

1 a) Copy and complete the following passage choosing words from this list to fill in the blanks:

> carbohydrate   carbon dioxide   chlorophyll   complicated
> glucose   leaves   light   photosynthesis   oxygen   small
> Sun   waste   water

Green plants take in _____ simple molecules and convert them into the large _____ ones they need for food. The making of food by green plants is called _____. The process uses _____ energy from the _____. The energy is trapped by the _____ in the leaves. Two simple raw materials are involved in the process, _____ from the air and _____ from the soil. It takes place mainly in the _____ of the plant. The most common kind of food produced is _____ which is a _____. The gas _____ is a _____ product of the process.

b) Why is this process which takes place in green plants called *photo*synthesis?

2 Plants use the sugars that they make by photosynthesis to make all the other large complicated molecules that they need. Here are some examples:

> amino acids   cellulose   chlorophyll   starch

Which of these examples

a) is needed to make cell walls

b) acts as a food store

c) are needed to make proteins

d) is contained in chloroplasts?

3   Some of the glucose made by photosynthesis is oxidised in respiration to provide
energy for the plant.

   a)   Write down an equation for the oxidation of glucose in respiration in either
        words or symbols.

   b)   Describe two activities for which a plant needs the energy from respiration.

4   Many useful products are obtained from plants.

   a)   Name *two* plants grown for their vegetable oil. From which part of the plant does
        the oil come?

   b)   Which plants are grown to make sugar?

   c)   Perfumes are made using oils from plants. Give *one* example of a plant used to
        make perfume.

   d)   Name *two* drugs obtained from plants.

   e)   Why do we depend on plants for the meat in our diets as well as for the
        vegetables?

   f)   Give some examples of herbs and spices obtained from plants.

   g)   What is paper made from?

   h)   Why should people be encouraged to use recycled paper?

   i)   Make a list of *ten* plants whose products are useful for some purpose other than
        food.

5   A student placed some breadcrumbs in a test tube, added an equal amount of
copper (II) oxide powder, and mixed the contents. A delivery bend was fitted and the
tube and contents were heated. A second test tube of limewater (calcium hydroxide
solution) was held just below the delivery bend.

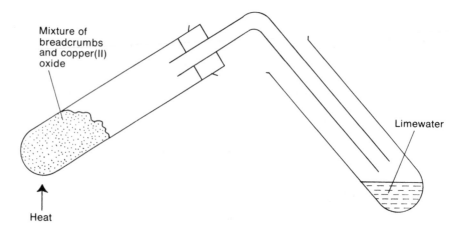

Mixture of
breadcrumbs
and copper(II)
oxide

Limewater

Heat

After a few minutes, droplets of a colourless liquid were seen in the delivery bend, and the limewater turned cloudy near the surface. The colourless liquid turned anhydrous copper (II) sulphate from white to blue.

a) What liquid was present in the delivery bend?

b) How could you show that the liquid was pure?

c) Name the gas produced in this test which turns limewater milky.

d) Explain how these results demonstrate that carbon and hydrogen are present in the substances contained in breadcrumbs.

e) Explain why it is not possible to conclude that oxygen is present in the substances contained in breadcrumbs.

f) What is a **carbohydrate**?

6 Copy and complete the following table by giving details about tests for glucose and starch.

	Glucose	Starch
What is the testing reagent? How much reagent is needed to test 2 cm^3 of solution? Is heat required? What is the colour of a positive test?		

7 This diagram shows how carbohydrates are interchangeable.

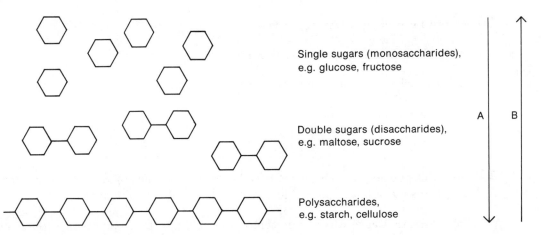

Single sugars (monosaccharides), e.g. glucose, fructose

Double sugars (disaccharides), e.g. maltose, sucrose

Polysaccharides, e.g. starch, cellulose

a) Copy the diagram.

b) What type of reaction is represented by arrow A on the diagram?

c) What type of reaction is represented by arrow B on the diagram?

8 Carbohydrates, fats and proteins are important classes of compounds found in living organisms.

Copy and complete this table by placing a tick under each element that is found in the foods given:

	Carbon	Hydrogen	Oxygen	Nitrogen
Carbohydrate				
Protein				
Fat				

9 Copy and complete these sentences about **proteins**:

a) Proteins are made up of smaller units called _____.

b) About _____ different amino acids occur in nature.

c) Small chains of amino acids are called _____.

d) Some proteins are tough and fibre-like, forming structures such as hair, _____ and _____.

e) Substances called _____ are proteins that control the rate of chemical reactions in the body.

10 A test for proteins is the **biuret test**.

a) Which two reagents are used in this test?

b) Describe how you would use them to test 2 cm^3 of a solution for protein.

c) What is the result of a positive test?

11 a) Milk powder, when heated with soda lime (a strong alkali), releases a gas which turns moist litmus paper blue. What is the likely identity of the gas?

b) What substance which is present in the milk powder could act as a source of nitrogen in this test?

c) Which foods in the following list would also produce the same result in this test?

   egg white   margarine   glucose   starch   cheese

15 The structures of three amino acids are shown below.

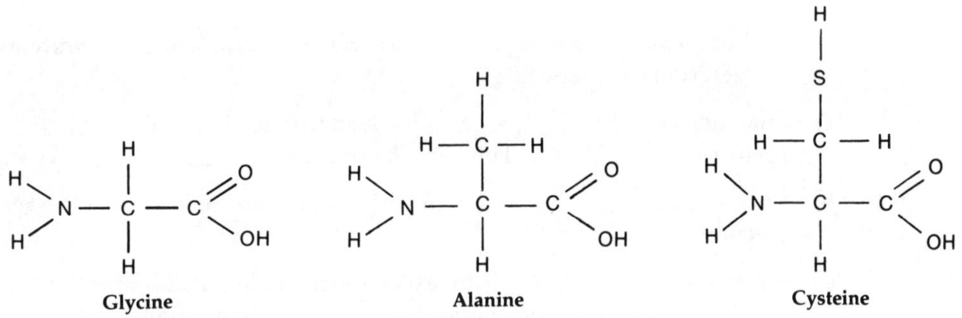

Glycine   Alanine   Cysteine

a) Which elements are found in all three amino acids?

b) Which additional element is also found in cysteine?

c) Write down the molecular formulae of the three amino acids.

d) In what ways are the structures of the three amino acids

  i) similar

  ii) different?

13 A pupil was given five powders A, B, C, D and E. Each powder was dissolved in water and tested for the presence of

  Glucose – using Benedict's test
  Starch – using the iodine test
  Protein – using the biuret test

The table of results below shows the final colour observed at the end of each of the tests.

	Powder A	Powder B	Powder C	Powder D	Powder E
Benedict's test	Orange	Blue	Blue	Orange	Blue
Iodine test	Black	Black	Yellow/brown	Black	Yellow/brown
Biuret test	Blue	Blue	Purple	Purple	Blue

Which powder contained

a) protein only

b) starch only

c) starch and glucose only

d) glucose, starch and protein

e) none of these substances?

14 Enzymes are an important group of proteins. Choose words from this list to complete the following sentences about enzymes.

> catalysts   destroyed   neutral   organisms   proteins
> reactions   specific

a) Enzymes are _____ which speed up the chemical _____ which occur in _____. They are 'biological _____'.

b) Enzymes are _____ in that they can only control one type of reaction.

c) Enzymes are _____ by excess heat and are also sensitive to changes in pH. Most enzymes work best in _____ conditions.

15 The following results were obtained from an experiment in which saliva was mixed with a starch suspension. Samples of the mixture were kept in water baths at different temperatures for 15 minutes. At the end of this time the samples were analysed to find out how much sugar has been produced in each. The results are given below.

Temperature/°C	0	10	20	30	40	50	60	70	80
Units of sugar	12	36	65	90	90	60	30	4	2

a) Plot a graph of these results drawing a smooth curve through the points. Label the axes as shown.

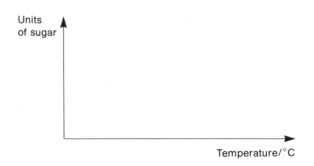

b) What kind of substance must be present in the saliva to break down the starch into sugar?

c) At which temperatures is most sugar produced?

d) Why is very little sugar formed when the saliva and starch mixture are kept at a high temperature?

e) What other factors, besides temperature, would affect the amount of sugar produced from a starch and saliva mixture?

f) Can saliva break down any substances other than starch? Explain your answer.

16 Look up the information required to complete the table below which shows some uses of enzymes. Copy and complete the table.

Use	Enzyme involved	Explanation
Washing clothes	Proteases	Biological washing powders dissolve protein stains e.g. blood.
Tenderising meat	Proteases	
Making syrup and fruit juice		Starch is broken down into sweet sugars.
	Cellulase	The tough cellulose cell walls are broken down.
Cheese making	Rennin	

17 a) The biological action of washing powder is reduced if the temperature of the wash is too high. Explain this.

b) Design an experiment to prove whether or not this is true.

3.2.3 **Chemical Reactions and Energy Transfer**

1 A type of disposable hand warmer consists of a polythene container surrounding a powdered compound. At the centre of the hand warmer is a second polythene bag, much thinner than the outer layer, containing water. When the hand warmer is squeezed, the water is released and mixed with the powder. A chemical reaction takes place, and the temperature of the hand warmer rises. During a trial, the temperature rose from 21 °C to 48 °C in 5 minutes.

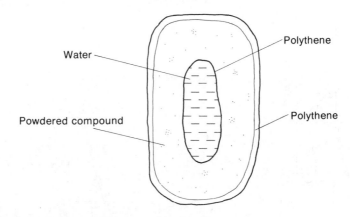

a) What was the rise in temperature of the hand warmer during the trial?

b) Is the reaction between the powdered compound and water exothermic or endothermic?

c) The table below shows the energy change in joules per gram, for four compounds A–D on reaction with water.

Compound	Energy change (J/g) on reaction with water
A	+312
B	−468
C	+68
D	−892

   i) Which of the compounds would be suitable for use in the hand warmer?

   ii) Suggest one factor, other than the energy change on reaction with water, which would influence the choice of compound.

d) One compound which could be used in the hand warmer is calcium oxide, CaO. It reacts with water according to the following equation.

$$CaO\,(s) + H_2O\,(l) \longrightarrow Ca(OH)_2\,(s) + heat$$

This reaction can be reversed by heating the product.

   i) Name the product of the reaction.

   ii) What hazards, if any, are there in using a hand warmer containing calcium oxide?

2

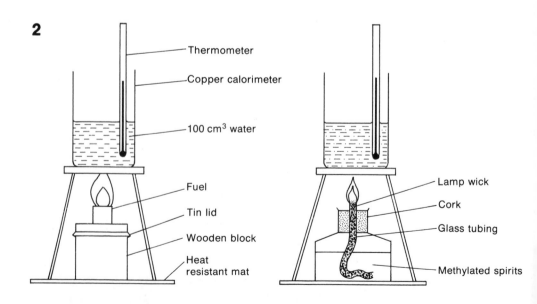

Alan carried out the following experiment to compare methylated spirits with solid fuel pellets for use with a small camping cooker. The solid fuel was burnt on a tin lid, while the methylated spirits was used in a wick burner. The mass of each fuel needed to raise the temperature of 100 cm³ water through 20 °C was found.

Results obtained in the experiment are given below.

Initial water temperature 19 °C
Final water temperature 39 °C
Mass of lid plus fuel (start) 25.30 g
Mass of lid plus fuel (end) 23.50 g
Cost of solid fuel (500 g) £4.00

Initial water temperature 19 °C
Final water temperature 39 °C
Mass of burner plus spirit (start) 120.25 g
Mass of burner plus spirit (end) 119.45 g
Cost of methylated spirits (200 g) 50p

a) Why is a copper calorimeter used, rather than a glass beaker?

b) Calculate the cost in pence per gram of each fuel.

c) What mass of

   i) solid fuel and

   ii) methylated spirits

   is needed to produce a 20 °C rise in the temperature of 100 cm³ water?

d) Which fuel is the best buy? Show how you arrived at your answer.

e) Write down two advantages and one disadvantage (apart from cost) of each fuel for use with a portable cooker.

3 A good rocket propellant, consisting of a fuel and an oxidiser, must satisfy the following requirements, among others:

1. The reaction between fuel and oxidiser must be very fast.

2. The reaction between fuel and oxidiser must be exothermic.

One useful propellant uses hydrogen peroxide (H_2O_2) and hydrazine (N_2H_4).

a) Which of these two substances acts as the oxidiser? Explain your choice.

b) The products of the reaction between hydrogen peroxide and hydrazine are nitrogen and water. Write a balanced chemical equation for the reaction.

c) The energy level diagram shows the starting materials for this reaction being atomised.

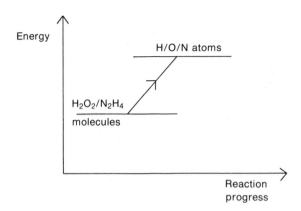

Copy and complete the diagram by showing the conversion of the atoms into the actual products of the reaction.

3.2.4 Rate of Reaction

1 Chemical reactions take place at a variety of rates. Some take less than a second, others a few minutes or hours, and some take place extremely slowly over many days.

Draw up a table with three headings, 'fast', 'moderate' and 'slow', and place each of the following reactions in your table under one of the headings. Justify your choice in each case.

> **Dynamite exploding**
> **Digestion of food in the body**
> **A dye fading in sunlight**
> **Toast burning**
> **The rusting of iron in a bicycle**
> **A silver trophy oxidising in air**
> **Petrol burning in a car engine**
> **Mortar hardening in air**
> **Baking a cake**
> **The formation of a precipitate, when solutions of silver nitrate and sodium chloride are mixed**

2 a) Copy and label the diagram below which shows the apparatus used to study the rate of reaction between marble chips (calcium carbonate) and dilute hydrochloric acid.

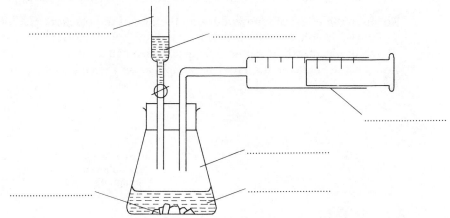

  b) The following readings were taken during the experiment.

Time (s)	0	15	30	45	60	75	90	120	150	180	210	240	270
volume of gas collected (cm^3)	0	7.0	15.1	27.2	38.9	54.0	70.1	94.2	108.1	115.4	118.6	120.0	120.0

  i)   Name the gas produced in this reaction.

  ii) Plot a graph of volume of gas collected (cm^3) on the y-axis against time on the x-axis. Draw a smooth curve through the points.

  c) At what time was the rate of reaction greatest? How did you decide?

  d) When did the reaction stop?

  e) On the same graph sketch the curve you would expect to obtain if the experiment was repeated using the same mass of *powdered* calcium carbonate.

  f) Describe how you could follow the rate of this reaction without measuring the volume of gas produced. Draw a labelled diagram of your apparatus, and state what readings you would take.

3 a) 0.5 g magnesium ribbon is added to a 250 cm^3 beaker containing 100 cm^3 dilute hydrochloric acid. A reaction occurs, producing magnesium chloride solution and hydrogen gas. Which of the following changes would *increase* the rate of reaction?

  i)   warming the acid prior to adding the magnesium

  ii)   carrying out the reaction in a 150 cm^3 beaker

  iii) using the same mass of powdered magnesium

  iv)   using 200 cm^3 acid of the same concentration

  v)   using 100 cm^3 concentrated hydrochloric acid

  b) Draw a labelled diagram of the apparatus you would use to measure the rate of reaction in this experiment.

4 When sodium thiosulphate solution reacts with dilute hydrochloric acid, a precipitate of sulphur forms.

$$Na_2S_2O_3(aq) + 2HCl(aq) \longrightarrow 2NaCl(aq) + H_2O(l) + SO_2(g) + S(s)$$

To study the effect of temperature on the rate of the reaction, Neil mixed 50 cm^3 sodium thiosulphate at 20 °C with 10 cm^3 dilute hydrochloric acid, in a conical flask. The flask was placed on a piece of paper, which had a cross drawn on it. Neil timed how long it took for the cross to disappear as seen by looking down through the flask.

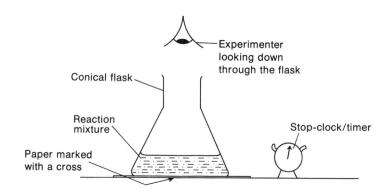

After writing down the time, he repeated the experiment with both solutions at a higher temperature. The results he obtained are given in the table below.

Temperature/°C	Time taken for the cross to disappear (t) in seconds	1/t
20	198	0.005
30	97	0.010
40	48	0.021
50	28	0.036
60	20	0.050

a) i) Name all the products of the reaction.

   ii) What caused the cross to disappear?

b) What effect does raising the temperature have on the rate of reaction?

c) Neil calculated values of $1/t$, where t is the time taken for the cross to disappear. Explain how this value gives a direct measure of the rate of reaction.

d) A 'rule of thumb' regarding rates of reaction states that the rate of a 'well-behaved' reaction doubles for every 10 °C rise in temperature.

   i) Do the results of this experiment agree with the rule of thumb?

   ii) Is the reaction well-behaved throughout the temperature range used?

5 Copy and complete the table, which compares enzymes with non-biological catalysts.

Enzymes	Non-biological catalysts
Usually catalyse only one reaction	
	Work well at a range of temperatures
	Only small quantities are needed

6 Hydrogen peroxide can be broken down by catalysts into water and oxygen. In an experiment to investigate this reaction, samples of fresh and previously boiled materials were added to samples of hydrogen peroxide in test tubes. Any gas evolved was tested for oxygen. The results are shown below.

Test tube	Contents	Test on gas evolved
1	Hydrogen peroxide	No oxygen evolved
2	Hydrogen peroxide + fresh manganese dioxide	Oxygen evolved
3	Hydrogen peroxide + boiled manganese dioxide	Oxygen evolved
4	Hydrogen peroxide + fresh liver	Oxygen evolved
5	Hydrogen peroxide + boiled liver	No oxygen evolved
6	Hydrogen peroxide + fresh blood	Oxygen evolved
7	Hydrogen peroxide + boiled blood	No oxygen evolved

a) What would you see happening in the test tubes as gas is evolved?

b) How would you test the gas for oxygen?

c) Why was Tube 1 set up?

d) Explain carefully what has happened in Tube 2.

e) Explain the results which occur in tubes 4 and 6.

f) Explain why the result obtained in Tube 3 differs from that in Tubes 5 and 7.

g) State *two* factors which should be kept constant in all seven tubes.

7   Each of the following graphs has 'time' plotted on the *x*-axis.

A 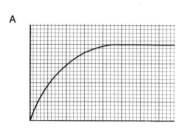   B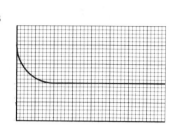

C 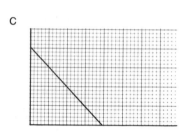   D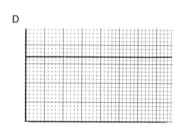

E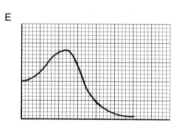

Which graph would you expect to obtain when the following are plotted along the *y*-axis?

a)   The volume of carbon dioxide produced when marble chips (calcium carbonate) react with excess hydrochloric acid solution.

b)   The mass of a flask containing zinc granules reacting with excess hydrochloric acid solution.

c)   The mass of manganese dioxide catalyst during the catalytic decomposition of a solution of hydrogen peroxide.

d)   The rate of reaction in a process where one of the products is a catalyst for the reaction.

3.2.5 Industrial Processes

1 Choose words from this list to complete the following sentences:

> milk   bread   penicillin   microbes   antibiotics   yeast
> protein   vinegar   biotechnology

a)   The use of microbes in industrial processes is known as _____.

b)   Butter, yoghurt, and cheese are made by the action of bacteria on _____.

c)   The flavour of different cheeses is due to the action of different _____.

d)   _____ is used to produce alcohol and to make _____ rise.

e)   In the production of _____, bacteria are used to convert ethanol to ethanoic acid.

f)   Bacteria and fungi can now be grown in special chambers to produce _____ as food for humans and animals.

g)   Some microbes produce substances that can kill other microbes and prevent them from multiplying. These substances are called _____. An example of one is _____.

2 Read this passage which is about micro-organisms as food for humans and answer the following questions.

> Bacteria can be grown to make a protein-rich food called single-cell protein (SCP). A variety of substances can be used by the bacteria to produce SCP. These include natural gas, methanol, manure, and food wastes such as citrus peel and milk whey. SCP is an excellent protein which can be produced quickly, in vast quantities. Its production uses little space and it can be easily stored as a powder. It is used at present as an animal feed for chickens and calves, but could be used for human consumption.
>
> Mycoprotein is a fungus. It contains about 45% protein and is high in fibre. It can be used to make artificial meat by adding appropriate flavourings. It has a texture which is chewy and similar to meat.

a)   What organisms are used to make SCP?

b)   Name one food waste used as a food base for SCP production.

c)   Give *three* advantages of SCP.

d)   Why do you think it is used only as animal food at the moment?

e)   What is mycoprotein?

f)   Why is mycoprotein more suitable than SCP for human consumption?

3

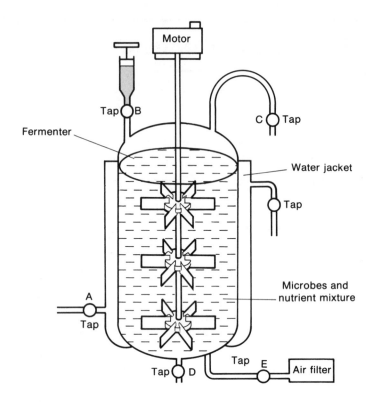

The diagram above shows an industrial fermenter. These are large containers in which microbes can be grown. There are many pipes and the taps are used to control the entry and exit of different substances.

a) Copy the above diagram.

b) Match the taps labelled A–E in the left-hand column with their correct functions in the right-hand column, and write out the corrected table.

Taps	Function
A	adding nutrients to the mixture
B	adding air to the mixture
C	allowing waste gases to escape
D	draining off the products
E	pumping cold water into the water jacket

c) What is the function of

i)   the motor

ii) the air filter?

d) Why is cold water needed in the water jacket?

e) When empty, the fermenter is pumped through with steam. What is the reason for this?

f) The fermenter can be used to produce mycoprotein. To do so, certain substances and conditions are needed. Copy and complete this table.

Substance or condition needed	Reason
Oxygen	
Sugar	
Ammonia	
Constant temperature of 32 °C	

4 In the **contact process**, sulphuric acid is manufactured from sulphur in several stages. Firstly, purified molten sulphur is fed into a furnace where it burns in air to produce sulphur dioxide. This gas is then oxidised further to sulphur trioxide, using vanadium pentoxide catalyst. When sulphur trioxide is absorbed in pre-prepared sulphuric acid, oleum is produced. Finally, oleum is diluted with water to produce more sulphuric acid than was present originally.

a) Using the information supplied, copy and complete the flowchart for the contact process.

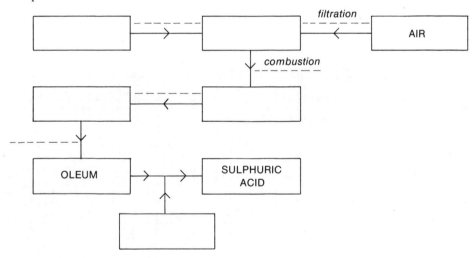

b) What are the formulae of the two oxides of sulphur?

c) Explain why the conversions

sulphur $\longrightarrow$ sulphur dioxide
sulphur dioxide $\longrightarrow$ sulphur trioxide

are oxidation reactions.

d) i) Describe two dangers arising from a leak of sulphur dioxide from the converter, one local and one global.

ii) Name another source of sulphur dioxide pollution.

e) Sulphuric acid is required for a number of important chemical processes. Name two materials which require sulphuric acid for their production.

5 Copy and complete the following sentences, which concern the Haber process for making ammonia.

a) The raw materials for the Haber process are _____.

b) Nitrogen and hydrogen are fed into the ammonia converter in the ratio _____.

c) The catalyst in the ammonia converter is _____.

d) Ammonia can be removed from the gases leaving the converter by _____.

e) Unconverted nitrogen and hydrogen are _____.

f) The formula of ammonia is _____.

g) Two important industrial uses of ammonia are _____.

6 Ammonia is a poisonous gas which is easily turned into a liquid. It is produced by combining nitrogen gas and hydrogen gas. The rate of production depends on the pressure applied to the mixture and on the temperature at which the reaction is carried out.

The set of graphs in the diagram below shows these effects.

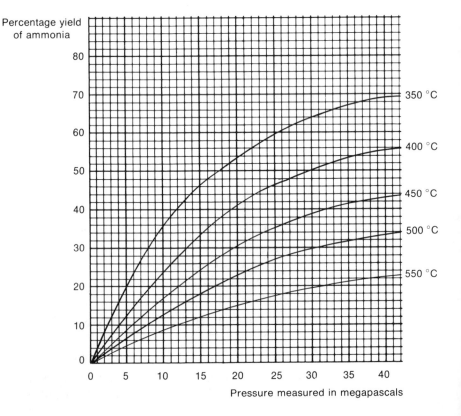

a) Use the set of graphs to help you answer the following questions.

   i) What is the percentage yield of ammonia produced at a temperature of 450 °C and a pressure of 35 MPa?

   ii) Describe the pattern linking the percentage yield of ammonia to the pressure.

   iii) Suggest what a manufacturer of ammonia should do to

      i) the temperature and

      ii) the pressure

      to increase the percentage yield of ammonia.

   iv) The conditions usually used are a temperature of 400 °C and a pressure of 20 MPa. Without changing these conditions suggest *one* way in which the yield of ammonia might be increased.

b) Much of the ammonia produced is converted into fertilisers. The three main elements plants require – nitrogen, phosphorus and potassium – are all present in 'NPK', a fertiliser made by ICI.

   NPK is made in the following way. Some ammonia is converted into nitric acid which is then mixed with phosphoric acid. The two acids are then neutralised with more ammonia and the solution is evaporated. Potassium chloride is then added to form granules. Finally the granules are coated to make the fertiliser free-flowing.

   Copy and complete the flow chart of the process shown below by writing in the names of the correct substances in the boxes.

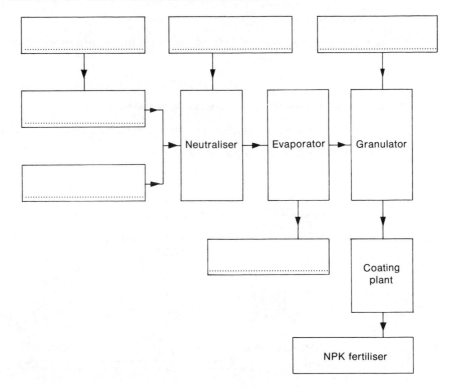

7   Nitric acid manufacture involves the catalytic oxidation of ammonia.

$$NH_3\,(g) + O_2\,(g) \xrightarrow[\text{catalyst}]{\text{platinum–rhodium}} NO + H_2O$$

This process was carried out in the laboratory using the following apparatus.

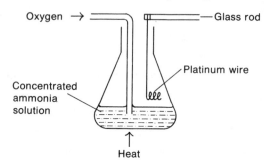

Concentrated ammonia solution was heated very gently while a stream of oxygen bubbled through it. A coil of platinum wire was heated in a Bunsen flame to red heat, allowed to cool then suspended over the solution as shown. The wire began to glow again. The experiment can be dangerous as ammonia will sometimes burn explosively in a side reaction under these conditions.

a)   What evidence is there that a chemical reaction took place?

b)   Write a balanced equation for this reaction.

c)   Ammonia will not burn in air. What feature of this experiment leads to ammonia combustion?

Before nitric acid can be formed, nitrogen monoxide must react with oxygen to produce nitrogen dioxide.

$$NO\,(g) + O_2\,(g) \longrightarrow NO_2\,(g)$$

d)   Suggest a source of oxygen for this reaction.

e)   Write a balanced equation for the reaction between NO and O_2.

f)   Give one large-scale use of nitric acid.

8   The cycle of reactions shows how three substances, calcium carbonate, calcium oxide and calcium hydroxide, can be interconverted.

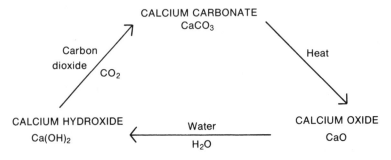

a) Name one form of calcium carbonate which is found as rock.

b) Name the gas produced when calcium carbonate is heated.

c) i) What happens when calcium carbonate is added to water?

    ii) What happens when calcium carbonate is added to dilute hydrochloric acid?

d) Describe one use of calcium carbonate in industry.

e) Suggest a method for converting calcium hydroxide into calcium oxide.

f) Describe how calcium hydroxide solution can be used to test for carbon dioxide. Write a word equation for the reaction which takes place when such a test is positive.

g) Write a few sentences about the use of calcium hydroxide in any *three* of the following applications:

    i) water purification, including effluent treatment

    ii) agriculture

    iii) steel production

    iv) tanning

9 The following diagram shows a **blast furnace**, which is used to extract iron from iron ore:

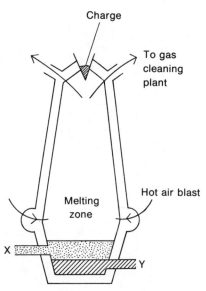

a) What are the three ingredients in the charge?

b) At which point (X or Y) is iron tapped off?

c) Balance the following equation for the reduction of iron ore to iron:

$$Fe_2O_3\,(s) + CO\,(g) \longrightarrow Fe\,(l) + CO_2\,(g)$$

d) The iron extracted from the furnace (pig iron) is very brittle and melts below the melting point of pure iron. Why is this?

e) Name two impurities present in pig iron.

f) Give two reasons for preventing the escape of the waste gases.

g) Hydrogen will reduce iron ore to iron. Why is this method not used on a large scale?

10 The diagram below shows how iron produced in a blast furnace is converted to steel.

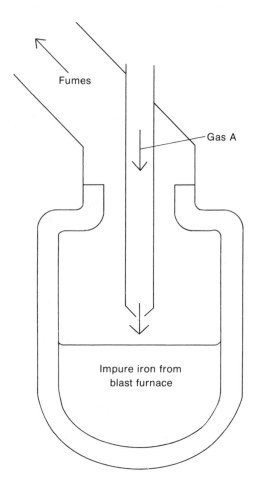

a) Name gas A.

b) i) One impurity present in the iron is carbon. Name one gas (other than gas A) which will be present in the fumes.

ii) Name one other impurity present in the iron from a blast furnace.

c) i) Which non-metal is present in steel?

ii) Name one metallic element that may be added to the iron during its conversion to steel.

11 Aluminium is extracted from its ore, bauxite (Al_2O_3) using electrolytic reduction in steel-walled cells as shown below.

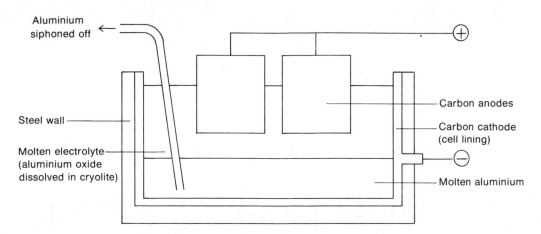

a) Copy the diagram.

b) What must be done to the bauxite before it is added to the cell?

c) Why is aluminium not extracted in a blast furnace?

d) What is the purpose of the cryolite in this process?

e) Explain why the anodes must be replaced regularly.

f) Why is there no need to heat the cell externally during electrolysis?

g) Balance the equations for the change occurring at each electrode:

i) Anode $\boxed{}$ O^{2-} $\longrightarrow$ $O_2 +$ $\boxed{}$ e^-

ii) Cathode $Al^{3+} +$ $\boxed{}$ e^- $\longrightarrow$ Al (e^- = an electron)

h) Explain why aluminium extraction plants are frequently sited close to hydro-electric power stations.

i) Give *three* uses of aluminium.

12 The diagram below shows a simplified diagram of a distillation tower at an oil
refinery.

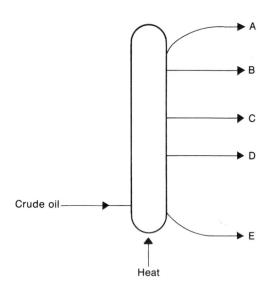

a) Each of the fractions described below was obtained from the tower at one of the
positions A–E. Make a copy of the diagram and at each position name the correct
fraction and its use(s).

Name	Boiling point range (°C)	Use
Kerosine	160–250	Jet fuel
Gasoline	40–180	Car fuel, raw material (plastics)
Diesel oil	220–340	Fuel for diesel engines
Refinery gas	40 and below	Camping gas
Heavy gas oil	350 and above	Fuel oil, tar for roads

b) There are a number of 'bubble caps' inside the tower at various levels, through
which the vapour must pass during distillation.

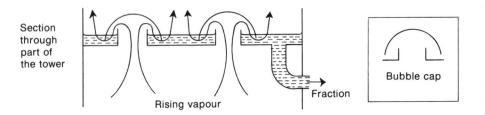

Explain how bubble caps help to separate fractions in the tower.

c) A part of crude oil used to make plastics is called naphtha. It contains **saturated hydrocarbons** with between 8 and 12 carbon atoms in each molecule.

  i) Explain the meaning of the words 'saturated' and 'hydrocarbon'.

  ii) Copy the flow diagram below which shows how naphtha is converted to plastics. Name processes 1 and 2 on your diagram.

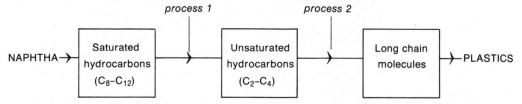

d) Copy and complete the table comparing fractional distillation of crude oil in the laboratory with industrial fractionation of crude oil.

Industrial fractionation	Laboratory fractional distillation
	Batch process
Separation improved using bubble caps	
	Fractions are taken from the top of the column

13 The following experiment was set up to carry out catalytic cracking of the hydrocarbon, paraffin:

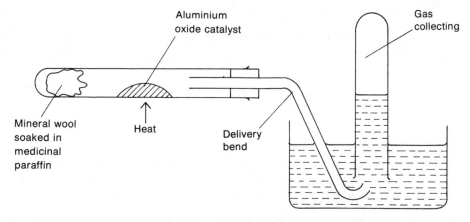

a) Once the heating has begun, it must not be stopped while the delivery bend is under water. Why is this?

b) Paraffin is a liquid alkane. Which gaseous alkane is used as a domestic fuel?

c) What happens to the paraffin molecules in the process of catalytic cracking?

d)   The paraffin used for this experiment was tested with bromine (in an organic solvent), together with the gas collected during the experiment. The results are shown in the table below:

Substance tested	Effect on bromine solution
Medicinal paraffin	No effect (remains orange/brown)
Gases collected during catalytic cracking	Bromine decolorised (turns colourless and clear)

What type of hydrocarbon must be present among the gases collected?

e)   Choose from the following list the correct description of the reaction between ethene and bromine:

neutralisation   addition   substitution   dehydration

f)   Why is catalytic cracking necessary on an industrial scale?

g)   The products of catalytic cracking undergo polymerisation. Describe what happens to the molecules in this process.

h)   What important type of material is produced in polymerisation?

14   The economics of some forming processes for the manufacture of plastic articles are compared in the table below.

Process	Cost of machinery	Speed of the process	Problems with the process
Compression moulding	Moderate	Slow	Excess material needs trimming
Injection moulding	High	Fast	Split mould gives joint lines on product
Vacuum forming	Low	Slow	Uneven thickness

a)   Small ice-cream tubs could be made by injection moulding or vacuum forming. Which method would you choose, and why?

b)   Suggest a thermosoftening plastic which would be suitable for making ice-cream tubs.

c)   Compression moulding is often used to produce plastic door handles and electrical switch housings. Which type of plastic – thermosoftening or thermosetting – would best suit these applications? Explain your choice.

d)   Which method would be most suitable for mass-producing nylon combs? Explain your choice.

e)   The forming methods above are all **batch** processes, while extrusion is a **continuous** process. Explain the meaning of the words 'batch' and 'continuous' as used here.

3.3 EXPLAINING HOW MATERIALS BEHAVE

3.3.1 Particles and Matter

1 Copy and complete the following sentences, choosing the correct words from this list:

> **atoms**   **electrons**   **ions**   **molecules**   **neutrons**

a) A sample of water contains many millions of H_2O _____.

b) _____ always carry negative charge.

c) Solid sulphur consists of a regular arrangement of S_8 _____.

d) _____ are found in atomic nuclei.

e) During electrolysis, _____ are attracted to the electrodes.

2 The diagrams below and overleaf represent particles of four substances which are undergoing changes:

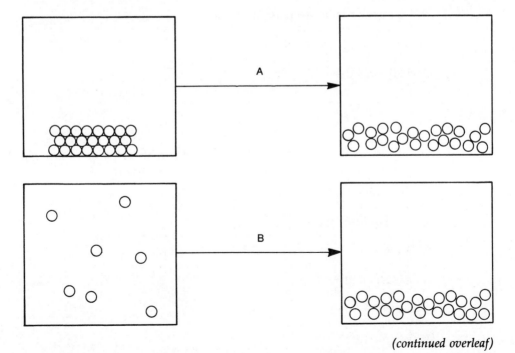

(continued overleaf)

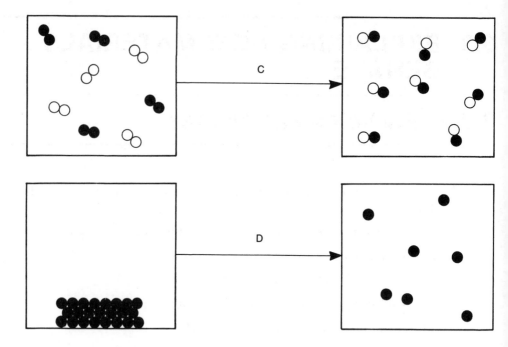

Which process, A, B, C or D

a) represents condensation?

b) represents sublimation?

c) involves a large decrease in density?

d) represents a chemical change?

e) is the reverse of freezing?

3 The diagrams opposite represent the arrangement of particles in eight different substances at room temperature. Which of the substances A–H

a) is a solid?

b) are liquids?

c) are gases?

d) are elements?

e) are compounds?

f) is a mixture?

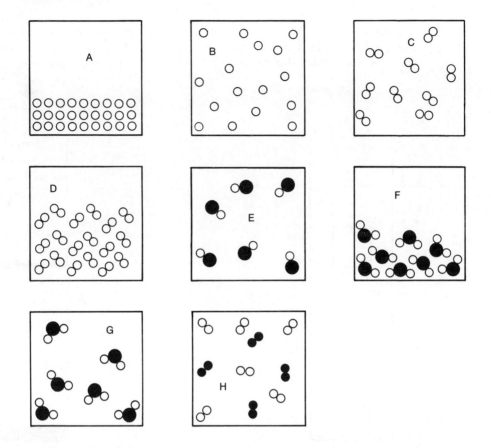

g) could be water (H₂O)?

h) could be iron (Fe)?

i) could be hydrogen (H₂)?

j) could be iodine (I₂)?

k) could be helium (He)?

l) could be hydrogen chloride gas (HCl)?

m) could be a mixture of nitrogen and oxygen

n) Draw a diagram to show what would happen to the particles in A if it were heated to just above its melting point.

o) Draw a diagram to show how you imagine the particles are arranged in carbon dioxide (CO₂) at room temperature.

4   The diagrams on the left below show what happens to an ice cube as it is heated using a Bunsen burner. The diagrams on the right show what happens to the particles (molecules) during heating, but the order has been changed.

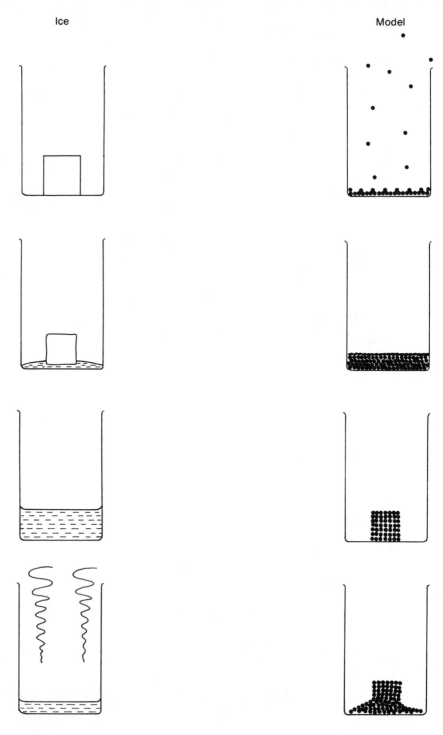

Ice   Model

a) i) Copy the ice diagrams in the same sequence.

ii) Draw the correct model next to each ice diagram.

b) As the liquid water changes to water vapour, the temperature remains constant. Explain what happens to the energy provided by the Bunsen burner.

5 A sample of ice was taken out of a freezer at $-10\,°C$ and left in a container in the kitchen. The temperature was taken every 2 minutes, until no further change took place. The temperature in the kitchen was $21\,°C$.

a) Sketch the graph you would expect to obtain if temperature (y-axis) was plotted against time (x-axis) for the results of this experiment. Add labels to show the melting point of ice and room temperature.

b) i) Mark a point 'X' on your graph where the kinetic energy of the water molecules is increasing.

ii) Mark a point 'Y' on your graph where the potential energy of the water molecules is increasing.

iii) Mark a different point 'Z' on your graph where the molecules are capable of vibrational movement only.

6 Explain the following:

a) When surgical spirit evaporates on your skin the area becomes cold.

b) A burn from steam at $100\,°C$ is worse than a burn from water at $100\,°C$.

c) Panting helps dogs to cool down in hot weather.

7 The following diagrams represent the arrangement of particles in a solid, a liquid and a gas:

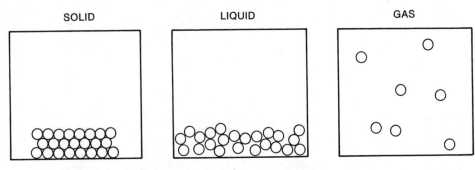

SOLID   LIQUID   GAS

a) Referring to the diagrams, explain why gases can be compressed easily but solids and liquids cannot.

b) Why does a bicycle with air-filled rubber tyres give a smoother ride than one with solid rubber tyres?

8   The apparatus shown below can be used to measure the expansion of a metal rod as its temperature increases.

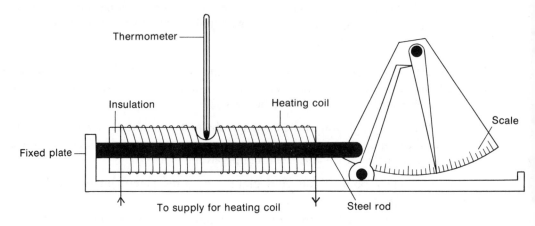

a)   Explain how the apparatus works.

b)   How would you calibrate the scale?

c)   Which instrument could be used to give a direct reading of the expansion?

d)   Describe how you would use the apparatus to measure the thermal expansion of a steel rod when it is heated from room temperature to 100 °C.

9   Explain the following observations:

a)   Steel girder bridges rest on a roller at one end.

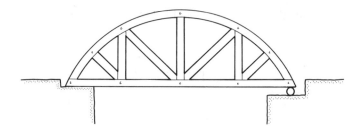

b)   Railway tracks are laid with a gap between them.

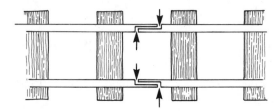

c) Steel pipes carrying steam are built with loops at intervals.

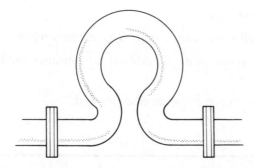

d) An automatic cut-out to prevent overheating at a position in a circuit can be made using steel and brass bars welded together as shown.

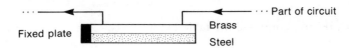

10 The diagrams below show the arrangement of atoms in a metal block at room temperature (298 K, 25 °C) and at 398 K (125 °C). The atoms are vibrating about their average positions.

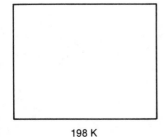

198 K

298 K

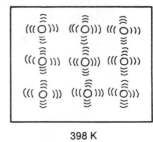

398 K

Re-draw the sequence of diagrams, adding the arrangement of particles you would expect at 198 K (−75 °C) in a way which shows:

a) the change in motion expected at this temperature

b) whether the sample has expanded or contracted compared to the situation at room temperature

Label the diagrams to indicate what they show.

11 All matter contains invisibly small particles. Explain each of the following situations by discussing the behaviour of these particles.

a) Small pieces of smoke, which appear as bright dots in a smoke cell viewed under a microscope, jiggle about a lot as they move.

b) Bromine vapour takes several minutes to diffuse through a container full of air, yet fills the container in a fraction of a second if the container has been evacuated beforehand.

c) A balloon inflates when air is pumped inside.

d) If a tin can with a tight-fitting lid is heated, the lid suddenly shoots off at high speed.

e) A metal rod expands when heated.

3.3.2 Formulae and Equations

1 Copy and complete the table below:

	Structural formula	*Molecular formula*

a)   H—Cl

b)

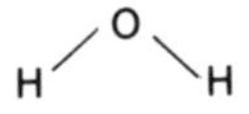

c)

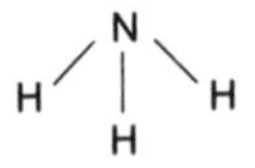

d)

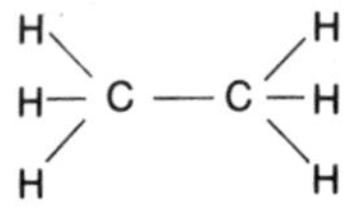

e)

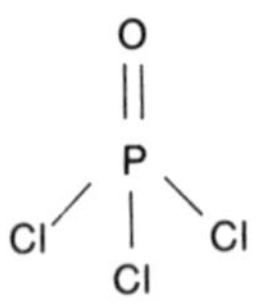

2 How many atoms are there in one molecule of each of the following compounds?

a) ammonia, NH_3

b) sulphuric acid, H_2SO_4

c) glucose, $C_6H_{12}O_6$

d) trinitrotoluene (TNT), $C_7H_5(NO_2)_3$

3 Ionic compounds are neutral overall. Copy the table of ion charges given below and use it to predict the formula of each compound a)–j).

Ion charge	+3	+2	+1	−1	−2
Ions	Aluminium Al^{3+}	Magnesium Mg^{2+} Calcium Ca^{2+} Zinc Zn^{2+}	Sodium Na^+ Silver Ag^+ Ammonium NH_4^+	Chloride Cl^- Hydroxide OH^- Nitrate NO_3^-	Oxide O^{2-} Sulphate SO_4^{2-} Carbonate CO_3^{2-}

a) sodium chloride

b) calcium oxide

c) aluminium oxide

d) silver nitrate

e) zinc sulphate

f) magnesium hydroxide

g) calcium nitrate

h) sodium carbonate

i) ammonium sulphate

j) aluminium hydroxide

4 The statement 'two oxygen molecules' can be written using symbols as $2O_2$. Copy and complete the following table by adding the missing statements or symbols.

Statement	Symbols
Two oxygen atoms	
	$4 H_2O$
One hydrogen molecule	
	$3 Cl^-$
Two ammonia molecules	
Three oxide ions	
	$2 H_2 + O_2$
A chlorine atom and a hydrogen molecule	

5 Write balanced chemical equations for the following industrial processes.

a) The action of heat on calcium carbonate in the extraction of iron in a blast furnace.

calcium carbonate $(CaCO_3)$ $\longrightarrow$ calcium oxide (CaO) + carbon dioxide (CO_2)

b) The conversion of sulphur dioxide into sulphur trioxide in the contact process for sulphuric acid manufacture.

sulphur dioxide (SO_2) + oxygen (O_2) $\longrightarrow$ sulphur trioxide (SO_3)

c) The production of ammonia in the Haber process.

nitrogen (N_2) + hydrogen (H_2) $\longrightarrow$ ammonia (NH_3)

d) The catalytic cracking of octane.

octane (C_8H_{18}) $\longrightarrow$ propene (C_3H_6) + ethene (C_2H_4) + methane (CH_4)

e) The catalytic oxidation of ammonia during nitric acid manufacture.

ammonia (NH_3) + oxygen (O_2) $\longrightarrow$ nitrogen monoxide (NO) + water (H_2O)

3.3.3 Chemical Calculations

---

1 Define the following terms:

a) Avogadro's number

b) 1 mole

c) relative atomic mass

2 What is the mass of:

a) 1 mole of potassium atoms

b) 10 moles of carbon atoms

c) 0.5 moles of silver atoms

d) 2 moles of uranium atoms

e) 0.001 mole of nitrogen atoms?

(Relative atomic masses: C = 12, N = 14, K = 39, Ag = 107, U = 238)

3 How many moles of each element are present in:

a)   24 g carbon?

b)   5.6 g iron?

c)   4.14 g lead?

d)   1.92 g copper?

(Relative atomic masses: C = 12, Fe = 56, Cu = 64, Pb = 207)

4 How many particles are there in each of the following?

a)   16 g oxygen gas (molecules)

b)   24 g carbon (atoms)

c)   390 g potassium (atoms)

d)   1.8 g water (molecules)

(Relative atomic masses: H = 1, C = 12, O = 16, K = 39. Avogadro constant: 6.02×10^{23}/mole)

5 Calculate the relative molecular masses of the following substances:

a)   hydrogen, H_2

b)   ammonia, NH_3

c)   sulphur dioxide, SO_2

d)   octane, C_8H_{18}

e)   phosphoric acid, H_3PO_4

(Relative atomic masses: H = 1, C = 12, N = 14, O = 16, P = 31, S = 32)

6 Calculate the percentage by mass of nitrogen in the following fertilisers:

a)   ammonium nitrate, $NH_4 NO_3$

b)   ammonium sulphate, $(NH_4)_2 SO_4$

c)   ammonium phosphate, $(NH_4)_3 PO_4$

d)   urea, CON_2H_4

e)   potassium nitrate, KNO_3

(Relative atomic masses: H = 1, C = 12, N = 14, O = 16, P = 31, S = 32, K = 39)

7 1.8 g magnesium was placed in a crucible and heated strongly. The heating was continued until no further change took place. After cooling, the contents of the crucible weighed 3.0 g.

a) How many moles of magnesium were used?

b) What mass of oxygen combined with the magnesium during the experiment?

c) How many moles of oxygen combined with the magnesium?

d) How many moles of oxygen would react exactly with 1 mole of magnesium?

e) What is the formula of magnesium oxide?

(Relative atomic masses: Mg = 24, O = 16)

8 A mixture of copper and sulphur powders reacts when heated. A·hard glass test tube was weighed. A sample of powdered copper was placed inside and the tube was re-weighed. A large excess of sulphur was then added and the contents mixed thoroughly. The tube was then heated strongly until no further change occurred. After cooling the tube was weighed again. A dark blue solid had formed. Readings taken during the experiment are listed below.

Mass of hard glass test tube	16.20 g
Mass of test tube plus copper	16.72 g
Mass of test tube plus compound	16.98 g

a) Describe the appearance of copper and sulphur powders.

b) Give one piece of evidence that a new compound has been formed.

c) What mass of copper was used in the experiment?

d) Explain why it was not necessary to record the mass of sulphur added prior to the reaction.

e) What mass of sulphur combined with the copper?

f) Calculate the number of moles of copper used.

g) Calculate the number of moles of sulphur which reacted.

h) What is the empirical formula of the compound formed?

(Relative atomic masses: S = 32, Cu = 64)

9 An oxide of iron contains 22.2% oxygen by mass.

a) How many grams of

i)   iron

ii) oxygen

are present in 100 g of the oxide?

    b) Calculate the number of moles of each element in 100 g of the oxide.

    c) What is the empirical formula of the iron oxide?

(Relative atomic masses: O = 16, Fe = 56)

10 Iron can be obtained from iron (III) oxide using carbon monoxide according to the following equation:

$$Fe_2O_3\,(s) + 3CO\,(g) \xrightarrow{\text{HEAT}} 2Fe\,(l) + 2CO_2\,(g)$$

    a) i) Calculate the mass of 1 mole of iron (III) oxide.

       ii) How many moles of iron can be obtained from 1 mole iron (III) oxide?

    b) What mass of iron can be obtained from

       i) 16.0 g iron (III) oxide?

       ii) 4 tonnes iron (III) oxide? (1 tonne = 1000 kg)

    c) What mass of carbon dioxide is released for every tonne of iron produced?

(Relative atomic masses: C = 12, O = 16, Fe = 56)

11 The equation below shows how glucose is produced from carbon dioxide and water during photosynthesis.

$$6CO_2\,(g) + 6H_2O\,(g) \xrightarrow{\text{light}} C_6H_{12}O_6\,(aq) + 6O_2\,(g)$$

    a) What is the relative molecular mass of

       i) carbon dioxide?

       ii) glucose?

    b) How many moles of carbon dioxide are needed to make one mole of glucose?

    c) What mass of glucose can be made from 22 g carbon dioxide?

    d) What mass of carbon dioxide is needed to make 36 g glucose?

(Relative atomic masses: H = 1, C = 12, O = 16)

12 A sample of glass has the following composition:

        silicon dioxide (SiO_2) 160 g
        sodium oxide (Na_2O)   31 g
        calcium oxide (CaO)   12 g

    a) How many moles of silicon dioxide are present in the glass?

    b) How many moles of sodium oxide are present in the glass?

    c) Find the ratio of silicon atoms to sodium ions in the glass.

(Relative atomic masses: O = 16, Na = 23, Si = 28, Ca = 40)

13 Halocarbons are compounds containing carbon bonded to elements in group 7 of the Periodic Table, the halogens. Some are used as refrigerants, dry cleaning solvents and aerosol propellants. An immersion heater was placed into a beaker containing a liquid halocarbon of formula $C_2Cl_3F_3$. The temperature of the liquid was taken every 30 seconds. The results obtained were as follows:

Time/s	Temperature/°C
0	16
30	19
60	23
90	27
120	31
150	35
180	39
210	43
240	47
270	47
300	47
330	47
360 (heating stopped)	47

a) What was the temperature in the laboratory at the start of the experiment?

b) What is the boiling point of the halocarbon?

c) For how long was the halocarbon boiling?

d) A joulemeter in the heating circuit showed that the heater was supplying energy at a rate of 2400 joules per minute. How much energy was transferred to the halocarbon while it was boiling?

e) During the time the halocarbon was boiling, 37.50 g were vaporised.

   i) What is the relative molecular mass of the halocarbon?

   ii) How many moles of halocarbon were vaporised?

   iii) Calculate the energy required to vaporise 1 mole of the halocarbon.

f) Why has the use of halocarbons as refrigerants and aerosol propellants been considerably reduced?

(Relative atomic masses: C = 12, F = 19, Cl = 35.5)

14 25 cm³ of ethanol was placed in a boiling tube fitted with a side-arm. An immersion heater was placed in the tube, which was fitted inside a polystyrene jacket as shown in the diagram.

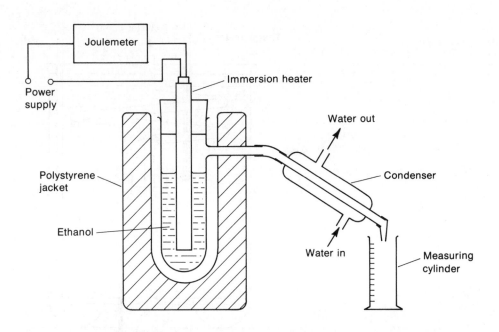

Once the ethanol was boiling at a steady rate, a 10 cm³ measuring cylinder was placed under the delivery bend to collect ethanol from the condenser. During the time that 5 cm³ of ethanol was collected, the joulemeter showed that 3.5 kJ of electrical energy was supplied to the heater.

a) Why was the boiling tube placed inside a polystyrene jacket?

b) If the density of ethanol is 0.8 g/cm³, calculate the mass of 5 cm³ of ethanol. (Formula: mass = volume × density)

c) The mass of one mole of ethanol is 46 g. Calculate the heat of vaporisation of ethanol in kJ/mol.

d) i) Why was collection of ethanol *not* begun as soon as some ethanol began to flow out of the condenser?

   ii) Write down two sources of error in this experiment, and state how the method could be modified to reduce them.

e) Would you expect the value for the heat of vaporisation of ethanol obtained from this experiment to be greater or less (numerically) than the true value? Explain your choice.

15 This question is about an experiment to determine the heat of combustion of methanol. A sample of methanol was placed in a wick burner and weighed. The burner was then transferred to the apparatus shown below.

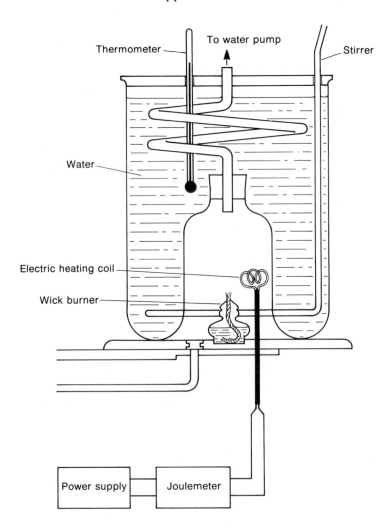

The burner was lit, and the water allowed to rise through 10.0 °C before the burner was extinguished. When the apparatus had returned to room temperature, an electric heating coil was used to heat the water in the apparatus, and a joulemeter used to find the energy input needed to cause a 10.0 °C temperature rise.

The results of the experiment are given below:

Mass of burner and methanol at the start	118.50 g
Mass of burner and methanol at the end	116.65 g
Energy required to give 10.0 °C rise in temperature	42 100 J

a) Calculate the mass of methanol burnt during the experiment.

b) Explain why it was necessary to stir the water continuously during heating.

c) What was the purpose of the water pump?

d) i)   How does this method compensate for heat loss from the apparatus?

ii) Name one other source of error in the experiment.

e) Use the formula

$$\frac{\text{heat of combustion}}{\text{of methanol}} = \frac{32}{\text{mass of methanol burnt (g)}} \times \frac{\text{energy released (J)}}{1000}$$

to calculate the heat of combustion of methanol in kJ/mol.

f) Write a balanced chemical equation for the complete combustion of methanol (CH_4O).

3.3.4 Structure and Bonding

1 The diagrams below show the structure of graphite and diamond – two **allotropes** of carbon.

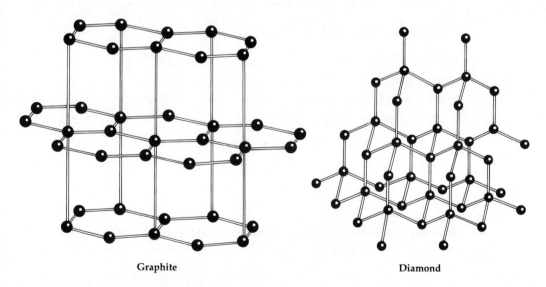

Graphite   Diamond

a) What are allotropes?

b) Copy and complete the following statements by choosing the correct word from the brackets. Use the diagrams above to help you.

i)   In a diamond, each of the carbon atoms forms four strong (covalent/ionic) bonds to other atoms in a (giant/layer) lattice. Although diamond is one of the hardest substances known, it is (malleable/brittle) because the forces between atoms act in a particular direction. As all four outer (electrons/ protons) in each (atom/molecule) are used in bonding, diamond is an electrical (insulator/conductor).

ii)   Graphite has a structure in which each carbon atom forms (three/four) bonds to other atoms. The forces within each layer of atoms are (strong/ weak), while the forces between layers are (strong/weak). This is why the layers slide over each other easily, and explains the use of graphite as a (lubricant/adhesive). Because there is one (proton/electron) on each atom which is not used in bonding, graphite is an electrical (insulator/conductor).

2   The table below shows some information about four different substances. Use it to answer the questions which follow.

Substance	Does it conduct electricity		Does it have a high melting point?
	when solid?	when liquid?	
A	No	No	Yes
B	Yes	Yes	Yes
C	No	No	No
D	No	Yes	Yes

a)   Make a key to identify the four substances.

b)   Which of the substances A, B, C and D is most likely to be

   i)   a metal

   ii)   a giant ionic structure

   iii)   made from small molecules?

c)   i)   Describe what is meant by a giant ionic structure.

   ii)   Give one example of an everyday solid which has a giant ionic structure.

3   The following table lists some properties of the five substances V–Z.

Substance	Melting point	Solubility in water	Electrical conductivity		
			Solid	Liquid	Dissolved in water
V	Low	Very soluble	Nil	Nil	Good
W	Low	Insoluble	Nil	Nil	–
X	High	Insoluble	Good	Good	–
Y	High	Very soluble	Nil	Good	Good
Z	Low	Reacts	Good	Good	–

    a) Which of the substances are metals?

    b) Which of the substances has a giant ionic structure?

    c) Which of the substances is present as ions only when dissolved in water?

    d) Which substance could be sodium?

    e) Which substance could be hydrogen chloride?

4 The diagrams below show the structure of five solids, A–E.

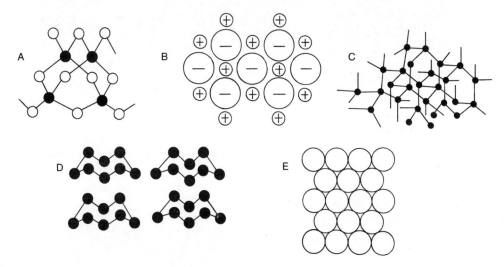

    a) Which of the substances are elements?

    b) Write down the letter of one substance which has

        i) a giant structure

        ii) a molecular structure

    c) Which substance will have the lowest melting point? Explain your choice.

    d) Which letter could represent the structure of iron?

    e) Write down the letter of one substance which

        i) conducts electricity only when molten or dissolved in water

        ii) conducts electricity as a solid

5 The structural formula of dichloromethane, a solvent used to remove caffeine from coffee, is shown below.

a) i)   How many atoms are there in one molecule of dichloromethane?

   ii) What is the molecular formula of dichloromethane?

   iii) What type of bonding is present in this compound?

b) Copy and complete the diagrams below to show the arrangement of electrons in atoms of hydrogen, carbon and chlorine.

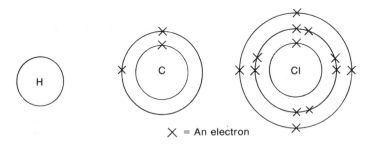

X = An electron

(Atomic numbers: H = 1, C = 6, Cl = 17)

c) i)   Draw a diagram to show the number of electrons in the outer shell of the carbon and chlorine atoms in a C–Cl bond in dichloromethane.

   ii) Which inert gas has the same electron arrangement as the chlorine in dichloromethane?

6 Sodium chloride (NaCl) is a solid with a high melting point. Carbon tetrachloride (CCl$_4$) is a volatile liquid which is used in industry as a solvent.

a) In which group of the periodic table is

   i)   sodium?

   ii) carbon?

b) The arrangement of electrons in a carbon atom may be written as 2, 4. Using this notation, write down the arrangement of electrons in an atom of

   i)   sodium

   ii) chlorine

c) What type of bonding is present in

   i)   sodium chloride?

   ii) carbon tetrachloride?

d) Draw diagrams to show the electron arrangement in sodium chloride and in carbon tetrachloride. The outer shells only should be shown in each case.

e) Name a solvent which will dissolve sodium chloride, and give a reason for your choice.

f)   Which of the following would you expect to be soluble in carbon tetrachloride, and why?

     iodine
     potassium bromide
     magnesium oxide
     iron

7   Copy and complete the table by correctly filling in the blank spaces.

Name of substance	Formula	Type of bonding
Hydrogen		
	Cl_2	
Water		Covalent
	NaCl	Ionic
Magnesium oxide		

3.3.5   Ions and Electrolysis

---

1   In an experiment to demonstrate the movement of ions, a crystal of potassium permanganate ($KMnO_4$) was placed on a horizontal microscope slide covered with a strip of filter paper. The paper had been soaked in sodium chloride solution. Each end of the filter paper was connected to a 24 V d.c. power supply using crocodile clips.

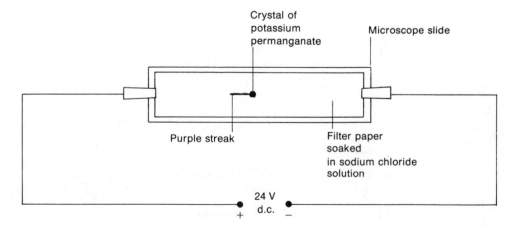

After 30 minutes, a purple streak 1.8 cm long was visible in the filter paper on the side of the crystal near the positive electrode.

a) Give two reasons why sodium chloride solution is a good choice for use in soaking the filter paper.

b) i) What is the sign of the charge on the purple ion in potassium permanganate? Explain your choice.

    ii) Explain, with reasons, whether the purple ion is likely to be K or MnO_4.

c) i) Calculate the speed of the purple ions in cm/s.

    ii) What would happen to the speed of the ions if the power supply was changed to 12 V d.c.?

d) i) If the crystal of potassium permanganate was replaced by one of copper(II) chloride, a blue solid, what would you expect to see during and after the experiment? Give reasons for your answer.

    ii) What would happen to the copper ions when they reached the crocodile clip?

2 The diagram below shows some details of the structure of a lithium atom.

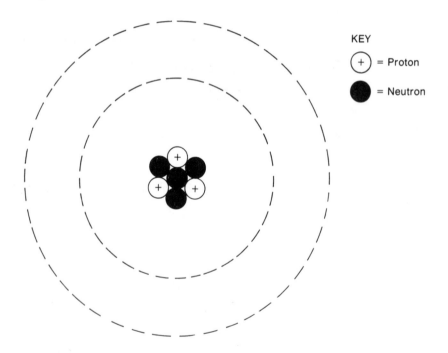

KEY

$(+)$ = Proton

● = Neutron

a) i) Copy the diagram.

    ii) Complete it by drawing in the correct number of electrons in each shell. Use the symbol ⊖ to represent an electron.

b) What change occurs when the lithium atom becomes an ion?

3 The diagram shows a key which can be used to identify some metal ions.

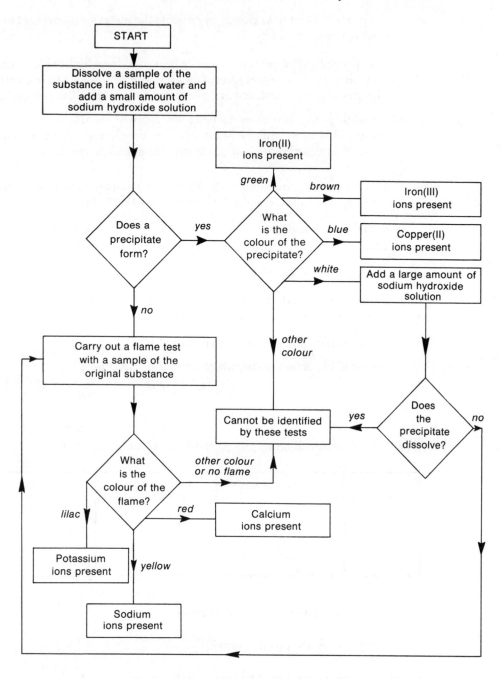

a) What property must all the metal ions have if they are to be identified using this key?

b) What is the name of the laboratory equipment that you could use to add only a few drops of sodium hydroxide solution to your dissolved sample?

c) Why should *distilled* water be used when dissolving the sample?

d) Use the key to identify as closely as possible the metal ion(s) present in each of the following compounds.

   i) No precipitate formed when a few drops of sodium hydroxide solution was added to an aqueous solution of the compound. A flame test was carried out on the original substance and the flame turned to a lilac colour.

   ii) A white precipitate formed when a few drops of sodium hydroxide solution was added to an aqueous solution of the compound. This precipitate then dissolved when more sodium hydroxide solution was added.

e) The addition of sodium hydroxide solution to an aqueous solution of iron (III) chloride results in the chemical reaction described below:

iron (III)   +   sodium   sodium   +   iron (III)
chloride (aq)   hydroxide (aq)   ⟶   chloride (x)   hydroxide (y)

where x and y refer to the state.

If all sodium compounds are soluble in water, then using only this and the information in the key, answer the following questions.

   i) What is the state symbol which should be used for x?

   ii) What is the state symbol which should be used for y?

4 Details of the composition of five particles are given in the table.

Particle	Number of protons	Number of neutrons	Number of electrons
A	6	8	8
B	8	8	6
C	6	6	8
D	8	6	6
E	6	8	6

a) Which of the particles is a neutral atom?

b) Which particles are positive ions?

c) Which particles are ions carrying a charge of -2?

d) Which particle has the greatest mass?

e) Which particle is an isotope of E?

5

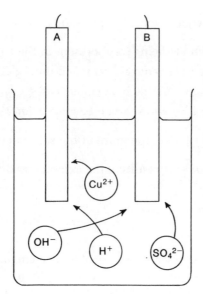

The above diagram shows the movement of the ions present during the electrolysis of copper sulphate solution. The electrodes A and B are connected to a d.c. power supply.

a) Which electrode is the anode? Explain your choice.

b) Which two of the ions shown combine to make water?

c) Which ions are attracted to the cathode during electrolysis?

d) Copy and complete the following table which lists the observations you would expect:

	Observations	
	Before start	During electrolysis
Anode	No change	
Cathode	No change	
Solution	Clear blue	Clear, paler blue

e) Why does the colour of the solution fade during electrolysis?

f) What would happen to the colour of the solution during electrolysis if both electrodes were made of copper? Explain your answer.

6 When a solution of copper (II) sulphate is electrolysed using graphite (carbon) electrodes, the following results are obtained.

Observations of		
anode	cathode	the solution
Gas evolved	Cathode coated with pink deposit	Blue colour fades, solution becomes acidic and warm

a) Name the gas evolved at the anode and the pink deposit at the cathode.

b) i)   Which elements were present in the solution at the start?
   ii) Which elements are removed during electrolysis?
   iii) Explain why the blue colour fades
   iv) Why does the solution become acidic?

c) Why does the temperature of the solution rise?

d) How would the results of the experiment differ if the electrodes were made of copper?

7   Lead iodide was placed in a crucible. The circuit shown below was set up and the power switched on. The bulb did not light up. Heating was begun and after a few minutes the lead iodide began to melt. Immediately the bulb lit up. Purple fumes could be seen coming from the anode, while silver coloured droplets appeared around the cathode. Heating was stopped and the contents of the crucible solidified. The bulb continued to glow.

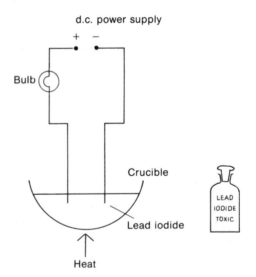

a) What *type* of particles are present in lead iodide?

b) Explain why the bulb lit up only when the lead iodide was molten.

c) Identify the purple fumes and the silvery-coloured droplets.

d) Explain why the bulb remained on after the contents of the crucible solidified.

e) What safety precautions are necessary during this experiment?

8 This question concerns the electrolysis of molten magnesium bromide.

Copy and complete the passage below, choosing the correct words from this list to fill in the blanks.

bromine	magnesium	anode	cathode	decomposed
lattice	ions	vibrate	move	electric current

The particles present in solid magnesium bromide are charged atoms called _____. As a solid, these particles can only _____ as they are fixed in a giant _____. Once the magnesium bromide is molten, the particles are free to _____ and can carry the _____. The positively charged particles of _____ are attracted to the _____, while the negatively charged particles of _____ are attracted to the _____. During electrolysis the compound is _____.

3.3.6 Radioactivity

---

1 The diagram below is a simple representation of a helium atom. The electric charge on each particle present is shown.

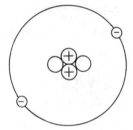

a) Copy the diagram and correctly label each of the following: nucleus, proton, neutron, electron.

b) What is the total charge of

    i)   the nucleus

    ii) the whole atom?

c) Copy and complete the sentence below to compare the masses of protons, neutrons and electrons.

    _____ and _____ are roughly _____ in mass, each being about 1800 times _____ than an _____.

d) Explain what is meant by

    i)   atomic number

    ii) mass number.

e)   A lithium atom can be described as $^{7}_{3}$Li. What is

   i)   the atomic number

   ii) the mass number of lithium?

2   Copy and complete the following table, which concerns alpha, beta and gamma radiations.

Radiation type	Mass	Charge	Identity
Alpha particle			Helium nucleus
Beta particle	$\frac{1}{1800}$ units		
Gamma ray		Uncharged	

3   Which of the three common types of radiation

   a)   consists of positively charged particles

   b)   causes the most ionisation in air

   c)   is repelled by a positively charged plate

   d)   is not affected by a magnetic field

   e)   is absorbed by thin paper or skin

   f)   is only absorbed by thick lead or concrete

   g)   is absorbed by 3 mm of aluminium

   h)   can be detected by a gold leaf electroscope

   i)   cause blackening of a photographic film

   j)   can be detected using a Geiger–Muller tube?

4   a)   What are **isotopes** of an element?

   b)   The diagram below shows an atom of the most common isotope of oxygen, $^{16}_{8}$O.

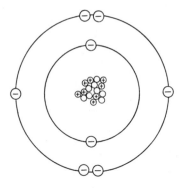

Two other isotopes of oxygen exist, $_8^{17}O$ and $_8^{18}O$. Draw similar diagrams to show the atomic structure of these two isotopes

c) Copy and complete the passage below choosing the words from this list to fill in the blanks (each word may be used more than once):

    unstable   **radioactive**   **rays**   **particles**   **nucleus**   **isotope**

All elements can have more than one _____. Many of them are _____. The _____ undergoes a change. When this happens α _____, β _____ or γ _____ may be emitted from the _____. This is called _____ decay.

5 a) Explain what is meant by the **half-life** of a radioactive isotope.

b) A sample of iodine-128 was monitored in an experiment and the following results obtained:

Time elapsed (minutes)	Count rate (counts/minute)
17	7080
29	5192
50	2816
60	2198
76	1364
105	662

The background count in the laboratory during the experiment was 80 counts/minute.

i) Explain what the 'background count' is, and list two contributions to it.

ii) Plot a graph of corrected count against time and use it to find the half-life of iodine-128.

6 The isotope $_6^{14}C$ has a half-life of 5600 years.

a) How many

i) protons

ii) neutrons are there in a nucleus of carbon-14?

b) After how long would a sample of carbon-14 decay to $\frac{1}{32}$ of the original count-rate?

c) Suggest why carbon-14 has been particularly useful in biochemical research.

d) Describe experiments using carbon-14 which show that

i) the carbon dioxide breathed out by a small mammal comes from glucose eaten.

ii) carbon dioxide is absorbed by a leaf during photosynthesis.

iii) sugars made in leaves during photosynthesis are transported to other parts of the plant in the phloem.

7 a) Radon has a half-life of four days. How long will it take for $\frac{7}{8}$ of a sample of radon to decay?

   b) Radium has a half-life of 1622 years. How long will it take for a 1.6 g sample of radium to decay until only 0.1 g remains?

8 A small domestic fire alarm contains a sample of radioactive Americium placed close to two charged plates. Smoke particles from a fire cause a drop in the small current flowing between the plates, triggering the alarm.

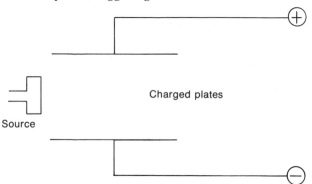

   a) What effect, due to the Americium, causes a small current to flow between the plates?

   b) Explain how the presence of smoke particles causes the drop in current which triggers the alarm.

   c) The operating instructions state that the unit should be wiped and vacuum cleaned carefully at least every six months. Suggest a reason for this.

9 Plastic sheet can be made by an extrusion process known as calendering. The thickness of the sheet, which must not vary too much, can be monitored using a radioactive source and detector as shown in the diagram:

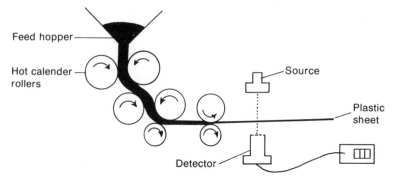

   a) Which type of source, alpha, beta or gamma, would *not* be suitable for this application? Explain your choice.

   b) What is the name of the type of detector commonly used to detect radioactivity?

   c) Explain how the source and detector can be used to monitor the thickness of the sheet.

10 Some forms of cancer can be treated using radiotherapy. Before treatment, the position of a tumour in the body is found. Two beams of radiation can then be directed at the tumour, each of just over one-half of the intensity needed to destroy tissue.

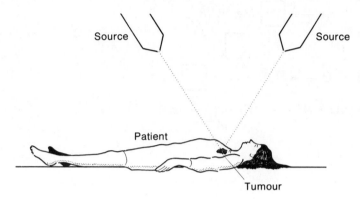

a) Explain why this procedure is of greater benefit to the patient than using a single (more powerful) beam.

b) Explain how rotating a single powerful source (or the patient) about an axis through the tumour is an equally useful method.

c) Why are the radioactive isotopes used in *diagnosis* almost always gamma sources?

11 Describe the use of radioactive isotopes in the following situations. In each case say

i) whether a suitable isotope should have a half-life measured in seconds, hours, days or years

ii) whether the type of source (α, β or γ) is important.

a) tracing leaks in underground pipes

b) revealing blockages in the human circulatory system

c) testing the thickness of cardboard during manufacture

12 a) Write down the following particle symbols and give the common name for each.

i) ^1_1H

ii) $^0_{-1}\beta$

iii) ^2_1H

iv) ^1_0N

v) ^4_2He

b) Draw diagrams which show the structure of particles iii) and v).

13 Copy and complete the following nuclear reactions.

a) $^{24}_{12}Mg + ^{1}_{0}n \longrightarrow ^{24}_{11}Na + \boxed{}$

b) $^{24}_{11}Na \longrightarrow \boxed{} Mg + ^{0}_{-1}\beta$

c) $^{3}_{1}H \longrightarrow ^{3}_{2}He + \boxed{}$

d) $^{236}_{92}U \longrightarrow ^{144}_{56}Ba + ^{1}_{0}n + \boxed{} Kr$

e) $^{7}_{3}Li + ^{1}_{1}H \longrightarrow ^{4}_{2}He + \boxed{}$